Casual Friday

THADDEUS ELLENBURG'S

Casual Friday
The Casuals

Volume One

Thaddeus Ellenburg

All the pieces in this book appeared originally on the podcast *Thaddeus Ellenburg's Casual Friday*—written and read by Thaddeus Ellenburg.

For the fans

(Current and prospective)

Contents

My Confession

Sitting in a center pew at the Holy Trinity Church in Culver Run with my wife and our two kids, listening to a sermon on repentance and still carrying the weight of that morning's breakfast ordeal, I'm reminded of all the terrible things I've done in my life up to this point. My conscience is heavy, and I feel it's time I come clean. This is my confession:

In the 4th grade, while enrolled in Miss Hooper's math class, I cheated on my long division exam thanks to a timid kid named Simon Wallace and his ever-giving generosity, a trait of his I took advantage of far too often. Last I heard, Simon was serving a two-year sentence at the Buddy May Correctional Facility for a similar offense and that his wife is a floozy. I feel awful about my actions. They were recklessly inconsiderate and unseeingly selfish—not to mention in poor taste, given Simon's handicap and the extra-large desk he occupied, making it easier to see off his paper. I still, to this day, cannot do long division, even though I work for the Panhandle's largest and oldest CPA group.

That being said, I would also like to confess to a Miss Dorothy Layman and a mistake I made on her '84 return. Looking back on it, I should have moved the decimal. She was right, and I owe her another zero.

In Maryville, Wisconsin, I attended a rock concert on the Justin Harlow Performance Lawn, and when the lead singer of the opening band came out on stage, he screamed with fiery intent, "Is everybody ready to rock?!" I shouted, "Hell yeah," at the top of my lungs along with the rest of my concert-going friends when, in fact, I was not ready to rock. I feel an overbearing sense of guilt for misleading all five original (and preceding) members of White Tongue, the crews that made that evening's concert possible, and the over eight thousand people in the audience that were, in fact, ready to rock.

My wife and I have been married for twenty-one years, and in the latter portion of our union (four years to be exact), my wife has asked me on a total of five hundred and sixty-two occasions whether or not an outfit makes her look too "hippy." Each time I put her worry at ease with a simple and kind, "Honey, you're crazy! You look wonderful!" I have lied to my wife on every one of these incidents and have been sitting with the weight of said deception for far too long.

At age eleven, while at my great-grandfather's wake, I gave a cookie to an unattended toddler sitting at the end of the buffet, only to find out moments later that the little fella was, in fact, diabetic. When confronted about what had happened, I blamed the occurrence on my second cousin's four-year-old, who was two years older and considerably larger—not to mention conceived out of wedlock with a man from the pet store. When my mother and I were alone, I exclaimed on the matter and the child I had just condemned, saying, "That one is bad news." I would like to confess to the two children involved and their parents, my mother, and the entire room of mourners and freeloaders (my apologies to both) on hand that day for Bingo Pappy's viewing. I'm just ill over the whole thing. However, in my defense, I would like to knock the mother of the diabetic boy for setting her child at the sweet end of the buffet table.

To Bill and Stacey Newgarden...I was the one responsible for flipping the orientation of the toilet paper in the downstairs bathroom during your dinner party last year. To make matters worse, I was the one who accused that nice-looking man with the green sweater and combover, bringing him into the foreground of everybody's suspicion. I stood there in the kitchen with the two of you after everyone else had left, making tasteless, schoolyard jokes about the man's backside and his wide pleated khakis, knowing good and well he was innocent, and I was the guilty one. I just feel horrible about the whole thing. My behavior that evening was vulgar and insensitive. It just plain stunk. I hope you can forgive me. Now that you know, I pray our relationship can move forward unbridled. Your friendship means the world to me, even though I think you're a couple of psychos for preferring the toilet paper under to over. You know it's touching the wall, right? And while you're at it, maybe look into a different kind of hand soap. Anything's better than that blue granulated stuff you set out for company. We all know Stacey steals it from the school where she teaches.

When my daughter was eight years old, she performed in a 3rd grade play entitled *Mr. Squirrel and His Nutty Friends.* During her big line, a man from the audience yelled, "Put some heart into it or get off the stage!" Well, honey...that man was me. That's why all those people were staring at us as we left the auditorium. And you were so cute...you thought, even at your young age, that they were feeling sympathetic toward you. You're so bright. When, in fact, they were fixated in wide-eyed gaze at your callous father. I can't tell you how broken up I am over the whole thing. It feels so wonderful to finally fess up to this one. I have not been looking forward to it at all. Then again, I don't know if I was entirely in the wrong that evening. I mean, sweetie...I love you more than life itself. You've turned into such a beautiful and well-rounded young woman, and I would never offer you a discouraging word—but you're a terrible actor. You have no talent. You can't emote. You couldn't move me with a forklift. And I'm a Pisces, for Pete's sake. There, I said it.

I rigged the '93 Shoeland County Watermelon Growing Competition, of which I was a judge. I gave blue ribbon recipient Albert Cox the synthetic agent to ensure his entry came out on top. Not to mention the fact that I made a killing in his victory. I put down a couple of C-notes on Albert via that rough-looking guy who's always smacking his gum in the corner of that place by the interstate. You know, the Corked Barrel? Moreover, I introduced a stunting serum to the submission of contest favorite, Charlie Paxton, which, moments before the judging commenced, had reduced Charlie's watermelon to the size and consistency of a rotten grapefruit. I got the concoction from that gypsy fella who owns the deli behind the carwash. I'm disgusted with my actions and feel sickened over the whole thing. My conduct was unbelievably dishonest and, frankly, inexcusable. I defrauded an entire town and cheated its hardworking citizens out of a long-lasting and cherished honor. I'd like to take this time to formally apologize to the following: The people of Shoeland County who trusted me, a seemingly impartial member of the panel and a man whose supposed passion for watermelon growing outweighed his quest for personal gain; the Shoeland County Farmers Association, who each year put on a hell of a contest that nobody can deny; and most importantly, Charlie Paxton. I robbed Charlie of his respected title, and because of it, people snicker openly at him in public and his children no longer call him daddy. Charlie has since given up watermelons altogether. And it breaks me up inside. He now works exclusively with figs—an embarrassing substitute that undeniably has rival watermelon growers rolling in their patches in full-blown hysterics. I just feel awful. Since I'm spilling my guts here, I see it only right that I confess all in the matter. My offense was less for profit and more for spite. In fact, this whole episode could have been averted had Charlie not campaigned against me to have the neighborhood trash pickup day moved from Fridays to Wednesdays. That SOB knew that I don't have to be at the office until ten-thirty on Wednesdays and that I sleep in that morning. And in addition, that I pay the extra seven-fifty to have the trashmen come up my driveway to retrieve the cans, which totally sit under my bedroom window. He said it was because his weekly Tuesday night "Daddies and Kids Neighborhood

Dinner" results in a lot of garbage. That's the first right thing that guy's ever said.

From May of '97 to November of '98, I walked around with a handful of fake flies in my pocket, which I used to get free meals at restaurants. I purchased them from Eddie's Joke Shop at thirty-five cents a fly (five for a dollar). I started small with soups and salads, then worked my way up to pastas. For a while there, I even did desserts. I once brazenly inserted a fly into a seven-ounce New York strip. I came up with this ingenious crosscut technique that, had it been used several times over, would have proven immune to detection. I'm sure it goes without saying I was the one responsible for the "Fly Fiasco" you undoubtedly read about in the papers during the summer of '98. Yes, I am the infamous "Fly Man." I can't begin to explain the shame and embarrassment I've been sitting with these past several years. I look at my family now and think of our nights out to dinner together and their smiling faces as they enjoyed a plate of chicken fingers before I distracted them with a mere, "Hey, what's that?!" and dropped a fly into their food. I was a little mixed up in those days. I had just received my poorest cholesterol report in years and had pretty much given up on life. There was a series of new restaurants in the area offering chowders and stews at an outrageous price, and well, I guess I flew off the handle a little. Actually, come to think of it, I wouldn't even consider what I did a crime. Six dollars for a bowl of chili? I mean, come on. Ten for a BLT? And I'm supposedly the criminal in all this. You know what? I don't regret a thing. I mean, not only did I save on over a year and a half worth of food, talk about a rush. God, I miss it!

Why, if I could, I'd walk right out of this service and down to Eddie's Joke Shop and get me a few dozen flies. If only it hadn't been turned into that male strip club. You know, the one next to the billboard with that blond guy on it with no shirt? The one that looks like he's eyein' ya while you wait in the turning lane. There's just nothing quite like filling up on a sizable portion of eggplant parm and half a bottle of wine and leaving the restaurant without even opening your wallet. Sometimes I got cocky and loosened my belt on the way out. Why, I'd sell my wife for a night just to chase that high.

Finally, I would like to confess my most heinous of transgressions to a Mr. Ernie Laughton, with whom I shared a train car from Los Angeles to Chicago last month. For two days, I convinced Mr. Laughton I was holding his family captive at an undisclosed location outside the city. I achieved a maximum level of verisimilitude using simple parlor tricks I picked up at a mentalist show I took in during my stay in California. I asked a series of straightforward questions, making it seem like I had knowledge and insight into his life. It worked brilliantly. I had never met this man before but was bored and had left my book back at the hotel. For forty-eight hours I played the gentleman kidnapper—cool and calculated. I made my demands in short and with little thought. Firstly, I asked him for his hat, then his tie, and eventually his shoes. I told him that if he tried to contact anyone on or off the train, I would notify my associate to carry out the deed. When he asked who my associate was, I panicked and blurted out, "Bob," the name of the guy that delivers the donuts to work each morning. Feeling sorry for putting this poor man through such anguish, I took Mr. Laughton to the dining car and treated him to dinner: salmon and asparagus with mashed potatoes from scratch. And by "treated," I mean we split the bill down the middle, and I took care of the tip, which I charged to Mr. Laughton—an expense that also included my meal. Old habits are hard to break. I'm so ashamed of myself. I can't begin to express how deeply remorseful I am. This truly is one of those proceedings I feel cannot be forgiven. I lie awake at night thinking of Mr. Laughton returning home to his family, shoeless and without hat or tie, greeting them with a loving and relieved embrace, and I can't help but think—If I had it to do all over again, I would have also taken his suit. Oh well; there's always next time.

Bring on the Communion!

A Study on Lesser-Known Insects

I t is no surprise that entomology is one of the fastest-growing fields of study. With over ten quintillion insects in the world, divided into one million different known species with an estimated thirty million undiscovered (shows what you know), the limits of research are boundless and presumably icky. Unbeknownst to Western scientists, researchers globally have uncovered a number of strange and alien-like specimens skulking in the nooks and crannies of Earth's most unforgiving places. Not unlike those lining up for the early bird at the J&W Cafeteria in Palm Vista, Florida. In fact, the only difference between the two groups is the ownership of a brand-new crumbled Cadillac. Now, more than ever, researchers are getting their heads out of the books and spending their days in the field. Unfortunately, it's the same field, and they're wearing down the sod around the fifty-yard line. The following is but a sample of these fascinating and sadly overlooked creepy crawlies:

The Austrian Tenor Beetle

Unearthed several years ago in the hills outside Kernsburg, the tenor beetle is roughly one inch long and emits a high-pitched hissing sound—particularly when seated behind the dugout of the visiting team. Discovered by premier authority on insect vocalization and hubbub (though he identifies more with hubbub), Dr. Alizah Horowitz—noted entomologist and author of *I Can Hear It, Can You?*—the tenor beetle produces a nocturnal tinging thought initially to be a mating call, but was later proven by Horowitz's successor, Dr. Eliza Flooganmeier, to be that of a chorus from Rodgers and Hammerstein—and one of the good ones at that. In a celebrated and now legendary display of melodic forte, renowned baritone Dagmar Stoopy performed an operatic duet with a tenor beetle to a packed house at the famed Denzin Hall in Lower Austria. The reviews were mixed, but all seemed to favor the performance of the beetle over that of Herr Stoopy, each echoing similar remarks, such as, "Not bad for a bug." In a rage, Herr Stoopy ravaged the beetle's tiny dressing room, which proved difficult given the singer's stubby fingers. Neither performer has sought reconciliation and is currently touring separately.

The Elephant Fly

The name of this speedy, little, five-eyed insect is really a misrepresentation—it's more a wasp than a fly. Native to the densely populated areas of the northeastern United States, it is a wonder this bug has managed to stay so elusive. With a long, thin proboscis used mainly for getting to the bottom of a brandy snifter, the elephant fly wears a black and white tuxedo with tails. In the summer, to avoid crowds and increase mating opportunities, the elephant fly migrates to the grass-covered shore dunes of West Sag Harbor, where it, over a period of hours, sheds its recognizable evening wear for something a little less formal—cashmere sweaters and open bathrobes. Its days are spent burrowing into the sand looking for carrion and civil war relics; while occasionally attending a local flea market—which, despite its name, consistently disappoints. At night, the elephant fly plays host to a spectacular light show of bioluminescence, which is irrefutably the best essence. A dazzling display of violets and greens illuminate the otherwise simple beach grass as it moves majestically in the wind— like an aurora borealis, grounded and forced to take later flight. At summer's end, the elephant fly begins the journey home, leaving behind its carefree thrills and promises to phone. The fly returns home thankful and with a newfound appreciation for its colony, thinking, *Where else can you get duck chow fun at three in the morning?*

The Chilean Satin Worm

The satin worm is blue with yellow flares and ranges anywhere from two to three hundred segments. It flourishes deep in the Valdivian rainforests and is the only worm known in existence to have antennae, which are used primarily for olfactory purposes and picking up the Friday evening radio broadcast of the *Venezuela Wrestling*

Hour. Revered by the ingenious peoples of southern Chile, particularly the Hoat 'n' Spaché, known for their picante mint stew, the satin worm produces a poisonous secretion that through the generations has been cultivated into a highly trafficked illicit drug. Initially developed for ceremonial and worship practices, "stain juice"—as it's been coined—is a one hundred million dollar a year business. Smuggled into neighboring Bolivia and Argentina alongside counterfeit key chains and elastic waist jeans, satin juice impairs cognitive abilities and temporarily paralyzes motor skills (which is most unfortunate for mechanics). However, the drug's most dangerous side effect is that of an increased impulse to perform dental work. And even more hazardous—a forgetfulness to bill immediately.

The Mung Bean Moth

The mung bean moth is two inches long and, unlike a typical moth, contains three sets of wings and a pouch for cold drinks. Much of this night-flying Lepidoptera is still a mystery to mainstream scientists. However, since its discovery a few years ago, documentation of the mung bean moth has been traced back to the early Vedas texts of ancient India. The following is an excerpt from one such hymn:

"Approach, O Protector of the Moong Bean, and lead us to the light. Incandescent or fluorescent, we seek with thee. Come, ye six-winged guardian, and bring hitherward snacks for the journey. Bring wealth to the cooler and helpest thy struggle. Destination drawing

nigh, O lofty friend, ruler of the backseat, sing forth Gentle praises to pass time anew. Deliver thy pasty delight, dehulled and ready for market. O Defender, keeper of the key to the pesticide shed, grant us thy sacred gift. Gather ye pods of plenty and grab a cold one for thee."

The Sunburst Caterpillar

Basking on the volcanic rocks of the Pacific's Keywala Island, the sunburst caterpillar is red with orange pompons and a yellow sash. It has two heads—one on each end—but, to no avail, shares a single brain. Much of the day is spent arguing with itself about which way to go and whose turn it is to wear the sash. A fruitless life (though there is the occasionally lime), the sunburst caterpillar finds pleasure in simple activities like eating Koduviscous flowers and licking discarded stamps. Its pompons, which develop in the early stages of adulthood, act as heat absorbers, which are essential in breaking down food and cutting down the energy bill. Local lore considers it bad luck to confine a sunburst caterpillar but says nothing about buying it dinner. In the final days of the caterpillar's life, it leaves its familiar lava-formed shore for a less familiar lava-formed shore via public transportation. Scientists are baffled by this strange behavior but are convinced it has something to do with it being a buyer's market. Nevertheless, the residents of Keywala City are plagued daily with overcrowded buses and slow-moving taxi lines.

The Sage Flower Mantis

The sage flower mantis is a particularly diabolical-looking critter with a trident-shaped head and a large frill designed to catch smaller insects and the occasional foul ball. It makes its home in dry and barren wastelands and other places like Sacramento. Suited for the heat, the mantis's head is ideal for opening bottles, while also functioning as a triple kabob skewer. With spikes covering its body to mimic thorns, this specific mantis camouflages itself by striking a contrapposto against the base of nearby shrubs. Only can a female mantis see through the disguise. The reasoning behind this is simply the distinct heat and smell put off by the male mantis—that, and the consistent winking. Similar to the sage flower mantis is the pricklyleaf mantis— a pointy, more brightly colored mantis with a diamond-shaped head and a serpentine posture. Dr. Ken Gensler, renowned mantis researcher and amateur bug novelist—whose works include the highly contentious, nevertheless praised *Gensler's Guide to the Mantis* and the more obscure, *A Tale of Two Cockroaches*—writes that the major difference between these two mantises is their aforementioned postures. Gensler states: "The Pricklyleaf conceals itself by achieving the more technically advanced S-curve stance where the Sage Flower seems to merely stumble into a weighted slouch." In a recent interview, Gensler was asked to explain his work's biased language. The illustrious researcher responded by jumping on his desk and performing a mazurka to the Polish ditty "I Got a Sausage, Do You Want One Too?"

The Eternal Tattler of Tinseltown

*R*ecent news of the Barker Company's deal for an immense tell-all about Tinseltown was met with equal parts excitement, indignation, and intrigue with the included announcement of its author—Gene Bottle, the pseudonym of a millenniums-old, Los Angeles area genie that claims he's granted over two thousand wishes for some of Hollywood's biggest names. The soon-to-be-published 323-page exposé promises readers detailed accounts and insights into the hasty and often shocking wishes made by the movie industry's wealthiest and most powerful men and women.

Unfortunately, little is known of its ageless author, who has already undergone a barrage of criticism from a growing list of film and television personalities. The Hollywood Privacy Board—a group of influential filmmakers and actors dedicated to spearheading gossip—labeled Mr. Bottle "the loose-lipped genie," publicly declaring their outrage at the Barker Company for "putting quarterly earnings ahead of their integrity." Mr. Bottle issued a response via Twitter, saying,

"I'm not a doctor, I'm a genie; and therefore, presumed confidentiality falls under buyer beware #geniefolklore." The Barker Company stood behind their decision by not only praising Mr. Bottle's character, calling him "uniquely qualified to tell *the* Hollywood story," but by also releasing several juicy pages of what has now been titled *Three Wishes: A Genie's Memoir.* Following are several excerpts:

In the spring of 1970, I emerged with great relief from my alabaster prison, urgently seeking a toothbrush and eager to hear of the Stones' success at Altamont, when I found myself in the presence of a Hollywood icon. Standing there before me on the soiled shag of a crumbling L.A. apartment was the haggard and unkempt remnant of legendary film actor Paul Keefer. Paul hadn't been in pictures since 1952 and, at the time of my arrival, had a dollar-nineteen in his pocket and was all but consumed by a severe addiction to cheese in a can.

"Are you here for the linens?" he asked, wheezing. "I can't get out the pimientos."

I informed him I was a genie there to grant him three wishes. He appeared distracted, perplexed by a mustard stain on his mustache that he tongued at periodically. After grabbing his attention with a flashy yet routine shape-shifting exhibition that included me morphing into an image of the once prestigious actor at age eleven and a '67 Impala, I communicated to him the standard wishing rules, clauses, and disclaimers, then asked him for his first wish. He stood there for a brief moment, vexed, with his tattered bathrobe ajar, before blurting out, "Cheesesteak!" At that point, I knew it was going to be a long night. Though, I can't say I was too disappointed in the request as I hadn't eaten in a year and always favored a bit of grease after a brief nap. After the inclusion of more deli meats in his second wish—this time a salami bagel with cream cheese and spring onions—I quickly realized, I would have to get involved. What can I say? I felt for the guy. So, keeping with the genie code, which forbids me from directly making a wish for a client, I suggested he make his third wish count and hinted at his current state and the blessed life he once lived. Alas, my efforts were futile in the wake of this now decrepit star as we sat down to our third and final sandwich—a Reuben with American cheese sauce. Unfortunately, transactions of this sort are all too common.

Once, in 1926, I was summoned by Fay Lawler, celebrated thespian turned silent screen goddess and sepia sex symbol, who wanted all the furniture in her Beverly Hills mansion re-stuffed and reupholstered—and done so without the aid of magic.

"I want a fabric that's unorthodox," she said. "Something the kids are into."

In those days, my eye for contemporary décor was passable at best. Not to mention, my work in textiles was primarily in rugs, particularly of the flying variety. But, despite my untrained and clumsy execution (which resulted in me smacking my thumb with a mallet causing it to swell and pulsate in a cartoonish fashion), her wish was granted. Regrettably, after the armchairs and love seats, I was tasked with polishing the silver, then told to head up to the roof afterward and get started on the gutters. After nine hours of cleaning, she put a nickel in my hand, checked my pockets to ensure I hadn't stolen anything, and reminded me to pick up more wood cleaner before returning the next day.

I spent the next seven years cleaning somewhere in the region of twenty-five homes as my oil lamp went from garbage bin to garbage bin. Film producer Lonnie Cooper, who lived down the street from Fay Lawler, had me dress up as a hotel chambermaid. He sat in the corner watching me clean and required after every chore that I butter and eat an ear of corn in front of him. Across the street, actress Debbie Mays wished for a grand swimming pool with an impressive fountain full of leaves. Then, to neither of our surprise, made me clean it. Actor Jerry Price had me mow his lawn and trim the azaleas. The azaleas were fine, but I struggled on the lawn as I have an extreme fear of open spaces. 1926 was a good year for kooks.

Incidentally, not all my clients are deranged. In fact, the majority of them are quite sound. That is, in the medical sense. Still, their wishes are focused monetarily and are almost always wasted on trivial desires. These wishes are often squandered indirectly when a client simply fails to think out a request thoroughly. They forget to consider the problematic reality of their wish. Take, for example, Leon Matthews, the hazel-eyed hunk from the TV series *Matched-Up*. Leon asked for the ability to fly, which I immediately granted him. And with outstretched arms, he took off like a jet, circling downtown and buzzing the boardwalk, scooping up cotton candy and churros. However, the following day, Leon was grounded at LAX for failing to meet FAA aircraft standards and specifications. The flying heartthrob was fined and required to lengthen his arms by twenty feet and gain a thousand pounds. The transformation was detrimental to his acting career. Leon Matthews is now a full-time aircraft for the sightseeing group Hollywood Charters.

Sadly, there's always an angle—a cosmic stipulation overlooked by virtue of enthusiasm and impatience. It's just the nature of the beast. And I simply hate it. By the end of most dealings, I'm viewed as a villain, a heel, or the product of some Rod Serling narrative. I'm nothing more than a magical creature of smoke and scorching fire, imprisoned within an oil lamp, trying to do his job as best he can.

I came to Hollywood in 1913 courtesy of a housing developer by the name of Walter K.T. Penny. I quickly found myself smack dab amid an economic boom fueled by mounting film studios and a horde of hopeful transplants. It was a wishing frenzy, and the number one request on everybody's lips was wealth and cinematic prestige—a request that remains my top seller. It's sad but true. People simply want to be rich and famous, which incidentally counts as two wishes. Clients are always throwing in "and" like it's a running list. Although there are the occasionally whack jobs, the cases that make it all worthwhile are the big ones—the ones that keep on giving to the clients long after the third wish has been granted. That's a line I used to toss around in my earlier days that I eventually adopted as a creed and began printing on business cards. These are the cases that transform a client's life and appear to everyone else as a self-made success story. And let me tell ya—Hollywood's full of 'em. I take a great deal of pride in knowing I have single-handedly made the better part of this town's more illustrious careers. (And I had a hand in the invention of paper!) One of my most notable successes to climb the Hollywood ladder—and to do so without touching a single rung—was film mogul and thirty-year studio head Oliver Davenport.

We met in 1927 at a wrestling match held at the Olympic Auditorium. At the time, my humble abode was used to oil up the athletes. Producer of such eminent classics as *Stage to Littlefield*, *The Oakwood Express*, and *Up the Shoal on a Steamer Built for Two*, Davenport was not only a key player in the financial growth of 1920s Hollywood and the development of a generation of young talent, but he was also an industry pioneer with his invention of both the micro-trailer and the twenty-five-hour studio clock. Davenport's strong suit was efficiency, and he made it his primary focus—an interest he pursued even after death. Davenport's will stipulated that his funeral was to take place on a sound stage with controlled rain, music cues, and a proper backdrop painting, all in hopes of keeping on-location burial costs to a minimum. He was to be laid to rest beneath the floorboards of Stage 17 at the base of his favorite scenery piece—a twenty-foot-high beer maiden from the Germanic farce *What's Up with Oodle?* The will also included a thirty-page script, breakdown sheets, and strict instructions for all mourners to stop by wardrobe for fitting before seeing hair and makeup.

In 1938, Davenport purchased his first restaurant, which he supplied with breakaway China and chairs in a ploy to cut operating costs and conserve dishwashing soap. He was one of the richest men in Los Angeles, and he kept his head above water during every economic crisis or industry upheaval. Hell, he didn't just keep his head above water; he all but hovered feet above it, profiting every bit of the way. During the war, while in production of *Codename: Mackerel,* Davenport began manufacturing firearms for sale to the U.S. Government. His company, Silver Screen Arms, mass-produced two models: a Springfield rifle that squirted water and a comically oversized M1911 pistol that, when fired, produced a red flag with the word "Bang!" printed on it. And he achieved it all thanks to his silent, fifty-four-hundred-year-old partner. Of all the private and intimate details shared in this book, I never thought I'd mention that one publicly. We genies are very sensitive about our age.

There was also 1960s comedy megastar Elaine Dunn. With two Ph.D.'s from Hampton—one in philosophy and the other in social policy (neither of which I can take credit for; that honor goes to a brother at the J.J. and Sons Printing Company)—Dunn struggled early on to make her mark in pictures. However, audiences knew her from her many television appearances performing standup. An exceedingly funny woman of unmistakable beauty and unrelenting grit, Dunn's only limitation was a bizarre speech impediment that made everything she said sound insincere; an exceptionally fortunate defect for telling jokes, but in the world of drama, she was far from convincing. Her romantic scenes were particularly sad and emasculated her most manly of scene partners. Actor Ford Dalton developed a crippling sense of self-doubt after a reading with the seemingly cynical actress and, as a result, took up a rigorous calisthenics program and developed an uncontrollable fear of limp produce. She had the bedroom stylings of a sarcastic lover, and it was taking her career nowhere and fast.

She tried every homemade remedy in the book—both editions, in fact. There was whipped cream and ham over easy, whistling with a mouthful of mayonnaise, and lining both sides of her esophagus with cod liver oil. She even made a donation to the National Phonetics Institute of her own accord after they reviewed her case and determined that her proposed treatment was asinine, senseless, and worth a shot. This all changed, though, with the simple snap of my fingers. In those days, I was on a big snapping kick. I didn't use to snap but had recently done some work for The Amazing Mindini and simply fell in love with snapping. Before that, for two thousand years, I would merely press the palm of my hand firmly on the client's forehead and push them to the floor while granting their wish. The last client I used this technique on was a circus ringleader that started his own religion after I granted him the power of mass perception and provided him with innumerable pieces of literature on federal tax exemptions. Nowadays, I do a swirling motion around their heads with some added pink smoke circling their body for a bit of flair.

Another more recent accomplishment was a young actor and singer from Iowa named Bo Simmons—a name now synonymous with achievement and worldwide acclaim. When I met Bo in 2009, after he came into possession of my lamp in a not so disappointing game of

Yankee Swap, he was represented by an unscrupulous agent named Mitch Haverton, who was known around town for exploiting many of his clients—and not in the good Hollywood way. He took advantage of countless rising stars, including the entire cast of the long-running TV show *The Junior Detectives Club*. Haverton sold their likenesses to a video game company that used the preteen crime solvers in their highly anticipated release, *Cannibal Island.*

"And what will be your first wish," I asked the young Mr. Simmons.

"I wanna be a celebrity!" he said with unbridled ambition. "And be wealthy and powerful and have millions of adoring fans and surrounded by beautiful women."

Again with the *ands*, I thought to myself. I suggested to the eager actor that we take things slowly. And so, one by one, we went down the list: Firstly, I granted him stardom—which took care of his want for wealth and power; then I gave him unmatched beauty—which took care of the women (that is, the half that wasn't already covered by the stardom); and lastly, in a heartwarming benevolent act, the future star took it upon himself to ask for world peace. I was floored. Sadly, my abilities regarding this matter yield to a chain of command that works in congruence with a long list of ideological infrastructures and belief systems. I regrettably informed the now well-heeled megastar that the universal wish for world peace was on backorder and already scheduled to occur on July 15, 2534, for a period lasting three and half minutes. Mr. Simmons seemed indifferent, then troubled in light of this new information. He took a moment then asked if it was too late to change his final wish to something a bit more immediate and practical, like X-ray vision or never having to worry about dry mouth.

18 Holes at Myers Creek

THE FRONT NINE

Nestled majestically against the Blue Ridge Mountains in the southeast corner of the Virginia Piedmont, the Myers Creek Golf Club has served as golf's most cherished and revered institute for nearly one hundred years. Like the links of Crab Hill or the Harbor Course at West Sag, the history of this 7,135-yard standard of golf excellence is as rich and immortal as the soil beneath its lush fairways—not to mention its club members, with an emphasis on *immortal* and a nod to premier healthcare. The course and its surrounding premises were built by famed designer Pat Lundy in 1921 on the site of a thriving bird sanctuary. It boasts a number of architectural features, including the lavishly decorated clubhouse of old-world charm where reputable golfer Bobby Thorson famously tried breaking his cummerbund by expanding his stomach during his speech at the 1956 Champions Dinner—or the commemorative Pinkerton Bridge, which leads golfers from the 18th fairway to the 18th green, where four-time Champions Tournament winner Greg Simon, during his final Champions Tournament appearance, graciously acknowledged the gallery with his signature peace sign before seven putting the hole and striking his caddy in the face with an egg salad sandwich. Still, Myers Creek's most celebrated and triumphant moments remain on the course, richly steeped in golfing lore. And with each hole named after a local bird, this 72-par time capsule packs quite the history.

Hole #1 – Virginia Mockingbird

A slight dogleg right, this opening par four offers a superb vista with an elevated tee and has without question witnessed its fair share of disastrous drives. One, in particular, came from the distinguished World War II admiral Norman R. McAllister during a late afternoon round with President Dwight D. Eisenhower.

After opting for a second helping of roast pork ham with apple jelly, two bowls of butterscotch ice cream, and four cups of coffee during a luncheon earlier in the day, the other members of the party were none too surprised when Admiral McAllister waddled up to his ball wheezing. He took three giant whiffs before losing his footing and was sent tumbling down the mound end-over-end, goose-stepping between somersaults. Eisenhower let out a bellow as the stoic naval commander landed in the center of the fairway like a lawn dart, with his head buried in the ground. A stickler for rules, Eisenhower insisted that Admiral McAllister not take a mulligan and play his second shot where it landed. Eisenhower then pulled rank and ordered Admiral McAllister to take said shot without removing his head from the ground. And so, with the posture of an ostrich, the undaunted war hero took a blind whack at his ball; and, to the astonishment of the other players, landed it a foot from the pin.

For the remainder of the round, President Eisenhower and the other members of his decorated foursome played every shot in a bent-over position with their heads swinging between their legs. After the men completed their round the following spring, they complained of severe headaches and an overwhelming urge to walk on their hands.

Hole #2 - Fox Sparrow

A straight 520-yard par five, Fox Sparrow is one of the more difficult holes on the front nine, even without the windmill—a decision made in 1942 in favor of the war effort and a shortage of aircraft propellers. The hole's difficulty comes from its undulating elevation and extreme slope to the left—that, and the fact that it sits downwind from the Caramel Candy Kitchen.

During the 1980 Celebrity Pro-Am, comedian Will Shepland— best known for his bawdy film parodies and reputation as an unabashed playboy—was drawn first and paired with the wholesome, strait-laced champion golfer Ted Noonan. After missing their second and third shots left of the green, with Noonan's in a pin-high bunker, the gallery readied themselves with stirring anticipation for a once-in-a-lifetime display of Noonan's skilled short game. As the 1978 Player of the Year stepped onto the sand and addressed his ball, he heard a young woman giggling from the gallery. He turned and saw, to his surprise, his partner, Mr. Shepland, with his arms around a bosomy, dark-haired spectator who was using the comical Casanova's 3-wood as a pogo stick. With his partner's noisy nuzzling in the background, the peeved yet focused professional took his shot with authority and stood poised in a shower of sand as his ball skipped past the pin and rolled off the back of the green. Noonan was livid. When he went to confront his partner, Shepland was all but missing. Noonan's caddy informed him that the comedian and his buxom fan had escaped the gallery and ducked behind a large bush. When asked which bush, the caddy commented, "The one that's bearing lacy undergarments." Shortly thereafter, Shepland withdrew from the tournament and retired to his fairway-side cottage along with his new, much shapelier partner, where he hung a little card from the door that read: "Hole in One."

Hole #3 - White-Breasted Sapsucker

A short, drivable par four, this hole not only yields low scores but contains a felonious history that dates back to the days of Prohibition. Chased from the mountains by clever and quiet-toed lawmen—especially when on their tippies—bootleggers sought cover for themselves and their illegal stills in the valley below. It was here infamous moonshiner Baggy Britches tunneled under the 3rd green and built his now legendary 3rd at Myers Creek still.

For two years, the cunning distiller operated without detection under the green's root system, producing gallons upon gallons of his tasty hooch. Sadly, productivity was halted when a group of golfers witnessed a thin column of smoke rising out of the cup. When the smoke subsided, the curious golfers peered into the hole and found a single eyeball staring back at them. Startled, the men leapt into each other's arms one by one until they were stacked four-tall. Baggy quickly fled the still out a secret entrance behind the green—a trap door covered in sod and concealed with a fake deer carpeted in a polished fur donated from the chin of Mrs. Britches.

When the marshal and his men entered the hidden still, they found a three-volume manuscript entitled "Cookin' with Britches," several crude drawings of what appeared to be plans for an illegal muffin shop, and forty-five gallons of top-shelf shine. As a memento, the Feds presented a gallon of Baggy's homebrew to the esteemed golf club, which then chairman, Elmer Aankins, placed on display inside the clubhouse, where the fermented contraband remains today. Of course, its proof has diminished slightly over the years, courtesy of countless late-night nips from the club's more prominent members. All of whom have admitted to replenishing the bottle with whatever clear liquid was readily available—cough syrup and denture soak.

Hole #4 - Crested Wren

A breathtaking par three surrounded by eastern redbud trees, with water at the front of the green, this half eight iron or full nine isn't a tough hole—unless it offers its notorious Saturday pin placement. To go at this flag, a golfer would surely have to have a combination of nerve, skill, and luck—or a meatloaf sandwich named after them at the nearby Lake Piedmont Mental Hospital. There have only been sixteen recorded aces, or holes-in-one, on Crested Wren during tournament play in the club's century-old history. The most notable occurring in 1926 at the Myers Creek Invitational, from golf legend and pioneer in the field of peat—particularly with his wildly successful invention of the steam-powered compost canon—Angus McSwiggon. The now memorialized tournament occurred during a pivotal time in golf history as the game's most respected professionals were adopting steel club shafts. However, McSwiggon believed in the tried-and-true wooden shafts, specifically hickory, and was determined to prove their superiority.

After a pretty up and down first two days, McSwiggon's third round had a particularly dismal start with two four-putts on holes one and two and a disastrous eight on hole three. Regrettably, McSwiggon was a bit of a hothead, known for taking out his anger on his golf clubs (and once on a bowl of red cabbage, which he consumed entirely in a fit of rage). By the time he reached Crested Wren, he had snapped the wooden shaft of every club in his bag, as well as several from the bag of his playing partner and the flagstick on No. 3. Some of the clubs he broke twice. When McSwiggion squared up the ball, his club of choice had already been reduced to a mere nub. On his knees, the gallery fell silent as he eyed his shot, drew back what was left of his club, and took a big one-handed scoop at the ball. Spectators and reporters alike exclaimed with surprise as the ball took flight and carried the water, then landed on the green and took a single hop straight into the cup. The shot came to be known as "The Miracle on Crested Wren." Not to be confused with the 1972 incident on Crested Wren where an unnamed boy brought back to life a dead deer by simply laying his hand upon it—and was later asked by the head groundskeeper to lay his hand upon several stubborn brown patches in the fairway at fifteen. Myers Creek recognized McSwiggion's shot with a humorously incongruous steel plaque, which they placed at the tee box of his timeless achievement.

Hole #5 - American Pintail

Especially beautiful in early spring when the magnolias blush with pink blossoms, American Pintail is a par four, dogleg left that offers one of the more troublesome second shots. After a forced layup off the tee, golfers are met with a challenging downhill second with an elevated green that slopes drastically to the right—not unlike the club's long-held stance on female membership. In 2009, Myers Creek opened the doors to its first female member, Congresswoman Deborah Roberts, after several prominent women's organizations rebuked the club's policies. The congresswoman's first day on the premises as a card-carrying member was a mostly welcoming one, culminating with a friendly nine holes between herself and 1999 to 2012 club chairman Dickie Jones—who, over the years, had been quite outspoken in his opposition of female members; not to mention sasquatches, which he felt was the next impending threat against club desirables. After playing the first four holes from the red tees, or "ladies tees" (aka forward tees), in a momentous act of defiance and equality, the congresswoman teed up her ball from the men's tee. The chairman was outraged. He scrunched his face and stomped his feet before dropping to the ground and throwing a full-blown tantrum. His caddy placated him with candy and pleasing stock market quotes. It was a revolutionary moment in golf history.

From then on, Congresswoman Roberts only played from the men's tees and lobbied exponentially for a reform of tee colors. Not wanting to abolish the use of multiple tees altogether, considering the different skill levels of competitive players, or "handicap"—language the hellbent crusader promised was next on the docket—the congresswoman proposed changing the red tees to magenta with a hint of plum and the white tees to anything but.

"I think we've seen enough white for a while," the congresswoman responded in a major golf magazine. "I say we change the color of the balls while we're at it, but one thing at a time."

After two years of in-clubhouse politics, Chairman Jones attempted to spearhead the congresswoman's efforts with a radical and unprecedented proposal or wily last-ditch scheme—whichever favored him more in the history books. Jones planned to give each hole two separate greens: a men's green and a much shorter women's green. The following day, Dickie Jones was called to step down as chairman of Myers Creek and asked to leave through the kitchen.

Hole #6 - Blue Pheasant

Absent of water hazards and sand traps, this straight and slightly uphill par four is one of the easiest holes on the course if you can keep your ball in the fairway. Lined with dense Leyland cypress trees, which can sometimes appear blue, hence its bird pairing, golfers collectively have spent hundreds of thousands if not millions of hours on this largely detested hole searching for their golf balls. In an item originally listed in the always amusing "Off the Tee" section of a 1981 Myers Creek newsletter, Blue Pheasant contains one of the course's more bizarre and astonishing accounts—even more astonishing than the bank accounts of most tour professionals.

In August of 1981, during a solo round, golfer Ryan Fitzpatrick hooked his drive into the anything but impenetrable wall of towering foliage on the left-hand side of the fairway. He entered the forest to look for his ball and was lost for nearly two years. Fitzpatrick built a shelter fashioned from golf clubs and khakis. He survived on granola bar rations and a pickle in a pouch he purchased from the clubhouse as a little treat for himself, even though his doctor directed him to avoid vinegar on account of his chronic acid reflux. When the rations ran out, Fitzpatrick steamed one of his golf cleats in a stew of leather and wooden golf tees. He tallied the days stranded on his scorecard and, as is the case with most scorecards, fibbed a bit because he was just, you know, having fun.

One day, the mentally and physically fatigued Fitzpatrick left his camp in a go-for-broke situation—but not before raking his footprints—and humped his golf bag filled with handcrafted provisions, including his already prepared second cleat, in an attempt to hike out of the harsh Virginia wilderness. Before nightfall, he reached the edge of the forest and found himself on the manicured grounds of a golf course. Unfortunately, it was the wrong golf course, and Fitzpatrick retreated back into the woods. He was found several days later by a Myers Creek foursome and their dog. When interviewed, the dog had no idea why he was there that day but could sense someone was in trouble.

Hole #7 - Northern Barn Owl

The longest par three on-course, Northern Barn Owl requires mid- to low-iron precision if golfers want to make it to the green in one. A whopping 195 yards, stretching slightly downhill and funneling toward an up-sloping green surrounded by sand, this hole is typically associated with high-scoring blips on the scorecards of most amateurs. That is unless they're the top amateur in the country.

In 1997, Myers Creek hosted the National Amateur Championship for the eighth time in the tournament's revered history—the most by any golf club where the clubhouse didn't sell firecrackers or fake IDs. The tournament favorite, NCU senior Matt

Kindler, who—after hitting the low opening round, which included a bogey-free scorecard, an ace on sixteen, and a peanut butter and jelly sandwich with the crust cut off—shocked the golfing community when he tied the course record of 63 on the second day. Kindler made it to the final pairing, which consisted of 36 holes of match play—nine in the morning and a full eighteen in the afternoon, and later, if time permitted, a movie at the mall with friends. Kindler's opponent—who, in his own right, played an extremely impressive tournament that rivaled the performances of most active tour professionals at the time—was brought to tears when the seemingly unstoppable North Carolina champion swept the first fifteen holes in an unparalleled showing of golf perfection. It was as if he couldn't miss, and his ball knew precisely where to go. Kindler walked onto the seventh with the score at dormie—which means he was ahead by the same number of holes left to play—and was poised to take the coveted title. After watching his opponent's ball hit the cart path and go rocketing out of bounds, it was nearly certain Kindler would be crowned the champion; it was only a matter of shooting par. Kindler addressed the ball with 4-iron in hand, took a dominatingly aggressive swing, and watched as his ball landed a foot under the flagstick. The gallery irrupted in thunderous applause.

As Kindler and his caddy walked up to the green, they were met with a standing ovation. A special honor that concluded abruptly as the congratulatory-turned-stunned gallery watched Kindler's ball inch up the green on its own, circle the flagstick several times, and drop into the cup. A committee of Myers Creek board members, along with a handful of eager R&D teams from the industry's leading companies, launched an official investigation into what newspapers were calling "Kindler's magic ball." When said ball was dissected, the committee— who expected to find a large magnet or small motor—found, to their surprise and horror, a nest of one hundred army ants. Consequently, Kindler was disqualified from the tournament.

Later in a press statement, Kindler admitted to not only using ant-filled balls during most of his victories but moth larva as well—a technique that he explained works on the same principle as Mexican jumping beans. Which, he also stated, gave him the necessary edge over his competitors.

In the weeks following the scandal, Kindler gave up the names of his suppliers, and a SWAT team was dispatched to the Click-Click Insect Ranch, where multiple arrests were made in addition to the ceasing of thousands of incriminating documents and the recovery of countless hollowed-out golf balls and corking paraphernalia. Detectives released a statement to the media claiming that they had uncovered an apparent insect cheating ring that had trickled all the way down to the junior divisions.

Hole #8 - Spotted Heron

Spotted Heron is a par four dogleg right that majestically wraps around the gorgeously serene Lake Lundy. With a stunning panorama of the surrounding mountains, golfers are met with a challenging tee shot to a small fairway target, of which most play it safe by choosing a low iron or 3-wood. It's the most nerve-wracking shot on the course. (Incidentally, the most nerve-wracking shot *off* the course are the ones taken at the chairman's daughter.) However, if a player can manage to keep their ball dry and land it in the fairway, they'll be rewarded with a much easier second shot courtesy of one of the largest greens on the course.

During the first round of a 2010 event, it was here winless golfer and worst on the money list, Doug Lament, amazed the sporting world alike when he made an unbelievable 189-foot putt—the longest in Myers Creek history. (As of the writing of this piece and certain publications within the pages of numerous respected golf journals and quite possibly the country's foremost weekly news magazines, the world's longest putt is recorded at 202 feet. Although, an attempt for an even longer putt began late last spring in Melbourne, Australia, and is expected to conclude next month when the ball reaches the hole. Onsite commentators and once junior- now senior-reporters all agree that the ball appears to be on the right line but collectively fear it may have been overcooked.)

After Lament's remarkably rare feat, the small-time golfer soaked up as much of the praise as possible and continued to boast of his putt long after the adulation had died down. In clubhouses and locker rooms, Lament—to the annoyance of everyone—recounted the putt repeatedly with enthusiasm and increasing cockiness. From bathroom stalls and standing in checkout lines to his wife's labor and their subsequent house foreclosure, Lament self-proclaimed himself the greatest golfer alive. He began heckling tour players during their putts and, after his dismissal from the sport, was eventually spotted at local courses taunting novice golfers from the bushes. The current whereabouts of Doug Lament are unknown, but still, to this day, golfers across the country continue to report the disembodied sound of hissing as they line up a putt.

Hole #9 - Nut-Brown Swallow

The front nine finishes in spectacular fashion with a magnificent 560-yard par five running up to the clubhouse, which offers the ideal spot for spectators to watch play from the veranda as they enjoy one of Myers Creek's signature rum and root beer floats. Stretching along the west side of Lake Lundy, Nut-Brown Swallow was not only the setting for a myriad of exciting pairings and storybook golf—including an albatross, or double eagle (meaning three under par on a single hole; that, or a surefire way to rig a coin toss)—but also bore witness to a dizzying array of clubhouse hijinks and unrestrained buffoonery.

One occurrence, in particular, took place on a spirit-filled evening in 1947 at the hands of Audrey Mannix—the nineteen-year-old, strong-willed Hollywood debutante and avid golfer. Mannix introduced herself to Myers Creek society with fabulous flair when she bared all in her now-legendary late-night swim in Lake Lundy. Growing listless from her table's Bordeaux-induced gabble, Mannix— in an effort to have a bit of fun by upsetting club decorum and needling its fuddy-duddy members—retired onto the 9th fairway with two-time Champions Tournament winner Greg Kessel, who was twenty years old and unmarried at the time. Kessel wrote of the account in his 1988 autobiography:

It was a sweltering evening, and the dining room was at capacity as usual. Jack Woolrich was up to his old antics. This time, animating the lobster on his plate in a drunken plagiarism of the Tramp, while Jackie Burr emanated her usual air of supremacy, which she apparently applied that evening with a paint gun. Then, out of the blue, the bewitching Audrey Mannix took my hand and whisked me away to the veranda. Not only was this completely unexpected, but my only other exposure to whisking was with a Denver omelet. She hurried off into the moonlit night and ran out onto the fairway. I followed. You don't not follow Audrey Mannix.

"Have you ever played strip golf?" she asked.

My entire body stiffened up like a board as I fell forward into a faceplant. I dusted myself off, and we began the most important game of my young career.

The rules were simple: Furthest from the pin lost an article of clothing. I remember bubbling over with excitement because Audrey Mannix was known throughout the club as being a dreadful golfer. Sadly, for me, she had been practicing, and I soon found myself down to my silk drawers. I was shaking from embarrassment. Audrey, who was fully clothed, must have felt sorry for me because with one shot remaining each, she offered to switch our scores, so to speak, in an all-or-nothing raising of the stakes if I got closest on this dreadfully crucial final attempt. I hit a flush seven that rolled within a foot of the cup. It was a thing of beauty. I made a particularly witty comment and started putting my pants back on as she addressed her ball. She drew back the clubhead and hit a gorgeous shot that landed just outside my ball. I instantly became giddy with excitement. She asked me to turn around while she tilted the score. I respectfully did so, but not without giving her a hard time about the shot, instructing her on her follow-through while I buttoned up my shirt.

"You want to make sure you don't turn over your wrists before impact," I said in a playfully gloating manner.

My heart raced at the sound of her undressing. Then, suddenly, I heard a splash. I quickly turned around to find a naked Audrey Mannix swimming in Lake Lundy. Well, I immediately started tearing away at my clothes to join her, when, alas, she stopped me.

"What are you doing?" she asked.

"What do you mean?" I said with a chuckle while pulling off my shoes. She smiled at me, cocking her head cutely to the side in that characteristic way that drove all her suitors wild and ever so sweetly reminded me that I had won the game. It was a crushing victory.

18 Holes at Myers Creek

THE BACK NINE

*C*onsidered the most magnificent and challenging venue in all of golf, the Myers Creek Golf Club remains the sport's most cherished and preeminent eighteen holes ever constructed. Its flawless and harmonious layout is an architectural wonder and has served as a century-old arena of sod, water, and sand for golf's most exhilarating and legendary moments. Like in 1987, when esteemed golfer and celebrity spokesperson for Little Lilly's Snack Cakes, Jensen Hughes, lost his ball on the 8th hole during an international match play event and was caught trying to replace it with a hard-boiled egg. Or the enduring Mother's Day victory from Senior Champion Ronald Belling, who—after walking off the 18th on his way to sign his scorecard—hugged and thanked his recently widowed mother before she smacked him in the back of the head for missing the birdie putt on thirteen. Containing the most iconic and stunning holes in golf, like the front, the Myers Creek back nine offers a significant and unforgettable glimpse into the club's storied past.

Hole #10 - Poplar Waxwing

The back nine at Myers Creek begins with a stunning and relatively painless dogleg left par four. At 450 yards, the beauty of Poplar Waxwing, like its name suggests, is accentuated by massive tulip trees and a community of American songbirds with an apparent fondness for country music—but not western; that would be silly.

The serenity of this easy birdie hole is a favorite for golfers looking to grab a quick bite to eat after the turn without disrupting play. Like Crab Hill's popular crab cakes or the zesty gumbo bowls at Sedge Grass Dunes, Myers Creek's signature staple is an open-faced sandwich the club playfully and affectionately calls "The Bird's Nest." It consists of country ham and cheese on Virginia toast (which is double the thickness of Texas toast), a scoop of black-eyed peas, half a pound of barbecue, freshly picked greens, a ladle of Brunswick stew, two fried chicken breasts, a slop of raw oysters, imitation crab (always imitation), ground peanuts with an apple butter spread, and is typically enjoyed with a warm glass of whole milk. In a 2009 issue, *Sports Cuisine Magazine* called it "a true tour of Virginia, with several stops at a number of the state's historic outhouses."

Arguably, no one over the years has been more a fan of the Bird's Nest sandwich than actor and singer Ricardo Valdez. Regarded as one of Mexico's most influential cultural icons of the past hundred years, Valdez took up golf during the dark, cocaine-fueled downswing of his career. Wealthy beyond imagination, Valdez, a man of advancing years, developed a God-complex and ignored the laws of the human body. He threw caution to the wind and filled his life with endless harmful habits, which resulted in a rapid deterioration of his health. He smoked several packs of cigarettes a day, abused countless drugs, and regularly overindulged—not to mention enrolling in numerous self-paced correspondence courses. It wasn't uncommon for the Latin megastar to consume several Bird's Nest sandwiches during a single round of golf or even have a crate of them delivered to him overseas. Once, while at his Los Angeles home, Valdez was seeking a late-night snack and reportedly boarded his private plane and flew to Myers Creek, where a chef was woken up to prepare the music idol his favorite sandwich.

In 1976, during a round at the prestigious golf club, Valdez ate three Bird's Nest sandwiches on the front nine, one at the turn, and another at the tee of Poplar Waxwing, before grabbing his chest and dropping to the ground. His manager jumped on the unconscious singer and started performing CPR while the rest of Valdez's entourage dumped the vast amount of cocaine from their golf bags. To speed up the process, one member dropped baggies onto the ground while another pitched them into the woods with an 8-iron. Despite their quick thinking, they had trouble clearing the trees, so they switched to a wedge. Valdez's loyal manager struggled to revive his friend and cash cow as the members of his selfless posse began to panic when their shots started coming up short. They chaotically yelled at the one taking swings—each franticly shouting different instructions simultaneously—like, "Square your shoulders and keep your head down!" Or "No, plant your front foot and follow through." Suddenly, Ricardo Valdez regained consciousness. He sprang to his feet, thumped his chest twice with his fist, and told his dumbstruck caddy to throw him his driver and another Bird's Nest.

Hole #11 - Red-Bellied Chickadee

The backstory of this treasured and impressive 130-yard par three is a long and fierce one. It's a hole that has been reshaped and rescaled over some fifty years—much like the hairlines of the club's board members. The original layout of Red-Bellied Chickadee began as a relatively straightforward, trouble-free hole and was a favorite of course architect Pat Lundy. When first constructed in 1921, this magnificent par three was without a single drop of water and had, for its time, a dynamically sculpted yet manageable green with sand to the left and plenty of room for players to miss right—a pedestrian design when measured against its present-day splendor.

Then, in 1923, Eleanor Lundy, wife of the renowned architect, approached her husband in her usual manner—sporting a pair of boxing gloves—and presented to him a profound reimagining of Red-Bellied Chickadee. A skilled designer in her own right, with ideas that most scholars have said outshined her husband's work in every respect, Eleanor proposed the first-ever island green—a green surrounded entirely by water. It was a pioneering marvel the likes of which golf course architecture would not see again until 1971 with the controversial brick chips trap and volcano-shaped putting green. As one might expect, Eleanor was met with her husband's typical disapproval and discouragement. And even though the famed planner secretly revered his wife's plan—calling it "genius" both in his diary and while mumbling in his sleep—he instead asked her to explain the lipstick on the collar of her blouse he found while doing the laundry. She informed him that the stain was, in fact, motor oil from the car he couldn't fix. Right then and there, Eleanor vowed to make her island green a reality.

Divorce ensued, followed by a lengthy legal battle, after Pat Lundy renovated the 11th at Myers Creek into his own version of an island green. Eleanor claimed ownership of the idea in court, while her ex-husband proved his innocence by stating the obvious differences in their designs. The "original" Myers Creek island green, built by Pat Lundy, was one foot in diameter and was particularly difficult for foursomes. Eleanor Lundy's green was 90 feet long and contained a beautiful stone and earth land bridge lined with vibrant flowers that gave players access to the green. Pat's green had no bridge, and golfers were forced to swim. After countless complaints of nibbling fish and water being tracked through the clubhouse, Myers Creek exercised their contractual right and sought course consultation and renovation from a third party: single white female Eleanor Lundy. The 11th at Myers Creek was transformed into its modern-day incarnation two years later, making it one of golf's most iconic greens.

Hole #12 - Tufted Bluebird

With the intimidating 11th behind players, Tufted Bluebird is a welcomed short par four with a wide and unbelievably forgiving fairway. As the events held at Myers Creek have evolved over the years, so have the broadcasting measures taken to telecast them. In 1983, during a televised charity tournament, actor Peter Pratt—the man behind the beloved children's television personality Giggles the Clown—left America speechless with his colorfully off-color on-air remarks, which, by the 12th hole, had culminated into a chorus of suggestive language and four-letter words. Additionally, unaware of the newly adopted zoom microphones being used to cover the event, while on-course, Pratt made numerous references to his involvement in illegal gambling—which included back-alley turtle races and betting on restaurant wait times, as well as the tournament itself. A fact that came to light when the Saturday morning star said to his caddy with a guttural laugh, "Watch me miss this shot and make a grand." Microphones went on to capture Pratt making favorable statements toward the hazardous materials and third-world working conditions involved in the manufacturing of Giggles the Clown merchandise, in addition to his hand in the unsolved assault on Flowers the Clown—a rival network clown that was whomped to within an inch of his life with rubber bladders by several masked assailants in a tiny car. Pratt was even filmed and recorded on his mobile phone, waiting to take his approach shot, placing an order for an escort and a large cheese with anchovies. (It should be noted that this was the first time in live broadcasting history that a public figure admitted to liking anchovies.) After walking off the green, Pratt was handcuffed, arrested, and allowed to make a single phone call, at which point he asked the detectives for the station's address so he could call the escort service and edit his delivery.

Hole #13 - Snowy Nuthatch

Not only the shortest par five on the course but one of the shortest on tour, Snowy Nuthatch is a perfect eagle opportunity for golfers before they tackle the challenging Perch and its daunting thousand-yard climb up the mountain. At a mere 470 yards, with a severe dogleg left and a clearable tree line allowing golfers to cut the corner and go for the green (or concede the hole to their friends and pay up by sucking the dirt from a worm), Snowy Nuthatch was the site of a golfing rarity—the inconceivable "condor," or triple eagle.

Only two other times in the history of golf has someone made an ace on a par five. The first took place in 1921 at the Shoreline Golf Club in Santa Barbara by silent film actor Sidney Ford. The popular actor waited for the perfect moment to publicly share his achievement, which arose during his annual estate bash seconds after his guests decided to relocate to a rival co-star's posh shindig down the street. The second happened in 1946 at the Aberdeen Golf Links by a senior member of British Parliament while in the company of his mistress. Unfortunately, when asked by the press about his miraculous shot, the prominent viscount indicated that a mistake had been made since he didn't play golf that day and instead took his wife on a romantic drive through the countryside.

The Myers Creek condor occurred in 1993 during a foolish round among college buddies in the middle of Hurricane Emily and was achieved in gale force winds with a sluggish 5-iron. Golfer Aaron Quinn pulled off the impossible when his drunken friends bet him fifty dollars he couldn't land his drive in the fairway while blindfolded. Quinn was up to the task. And even after a number of beers himself— fourteen and a half to be exact, as well as a quart of paint thinner—the determined amateur still had the state of mind to choose a club he knew he could hit straight; but sadly, was lacking enough sense to line up his shot correctly. Instead, the ripped weekend golfer aimed his shot some forty degrees off his intended target and inadvertently cut the corner and took on the flagstick. Thanks to the otherwise crippling winds, Quinn's ball carried the gap and soared out of sight. When the foursome approached the green, they looked up and down for their friend's drive until someone jokingly checked the cup. To their astonishment, there was Quinn's ball with his custom middle finger marking staring back at them. Quinn had executed the rarest event in golf and was not only too drunk to remember it the next day but also had to cough up fifty bucks.

Hole #14 - Hooded Vulture

This grueling uphill par four is the first in a historical and emblematic three-hole series known throughout the world and quite possibly beyond—say past the Milky Way in a galaxy with a cookie center—as The Perch. Considered hallowed ground for golfers and sports enthusiasts alike, there is no greater symbol of golf prestige than the Perch's two-hole push up the imposing Myers Mountain and its subsequent 16th par three summit. With a tee-to-green elevation change of two hundred feet stretching up the hill, the site of this taxing hole has a haunting and spooky past.

In 1878, long before Hooded Vulture and the development of the Myers Creek Golf Club—even before the area's flourishing bird sanctuary—legend has it a distraught and lovesick schoolteacher threw herself off the mountain. (Wouldn't it be funny if she was a schoolsick love teacher?) As the story grew, so did the rumored sightings of her ghost. Over the years, witnesses have reported seeing a striking young female in period clothing emanating a soft glow while walking the nearby grounds. Some have reported seeing her wiping down a missing chalkboard or doing cartwheels amidst the trees during the opening weeks of summer vacation.

In 1932, while enjoying a game of twilight golf, ill-famed and - fated Chicago gangster Jimmy Marbles, aka Dear Aggie, claimed he not only observed the star-crossed spirit but said he engaged with her in a delightful two-hour conversation. Jimmy Marbles was called "Marbles" because of his gravelly speech impediment, which, he alleged, the charismatic spectator corrected after a series of weekly tutoring sessions held around nightfall or the witching hour or whatever was good for her. The presumably touched yet now eloquently spoken racketeer quickly became known around the city's

South Side by a series of names. There was "Jimmy 'No Longer Marbles' Marbles," "Jimmy The Ghost Whisper," "Teacher's Pet," "Jimmy 'Bullets Don't Pass Through Me' Marbles," "Fruitcake Jimmy" (This was a name that was mistakenly in reference to another Chicago-area Jimmy who at the time was running around town swiping baked goods from store windows and leaving a calling card in the form of scattered crumbs), "Ectoplasm Jimmy," "Jimmy 'Yes, but What about Your Short Game?' Marbles," and most notably, "The Merchant of Intoxicating Spirits."

Hole #15 - Black-Shouldered Hawk

The Perch continues majestically up Myers Mountain with the jaw-dropping and especially strenuous par five known as Black-Shouldered Hawk. Ascending a seemingly unending 560 yards through an enclosure of lofty, sawtooth spruce trees with an unforgiving multi-tiered, back-to-front rolling green, this punishing hole demands both physical and mental strength if a golfer wishes to stay competitive—or simply make it back to the car on time where they promised to meet their lover after she finishes refilling the hot sauces in the dining room. And as if this wasn't exacting enough, Black-Shouldered Hawk is home to a colossal red spruce of dubious fame and celebration.

Given the name Pyke's Tree in 1962 by eminent sportswriter Atticus Hale, after the illustrious film director Samuel Pyke, this maddening Picea rubens was seeded on the edge of the left side of the

15th fairway and has been growing infamously at a twenty-degree angle for nearly a century—making it an absolute headache for any right-hander with a go-to left-to-right shaped shot.

Over the years, nobody has been more outspoken about their disdain for this coniferous hallmark than the tree's namesake—the late, mostly great, cinematic maverick, Samuel Pyke. Known by the public for his gritty and violent noir and war pictures, as well as marrying a baker's dozen of delectable A-list sweethearts over the span of his lifetime, Pyke found golfing notoriety after gradually being driven mad by this mammoth, needling nemesis. It didn't matter where the award-winning filmmaker's drive landed; his second shot always found its way into the branches of what ribbing club members occasionally referred to as "the sap trap."

In April of 1964, in a momentary lapse of self-control, Pyke famously climbed the contemptible spruce after it swallowed his ball. Pyke then proceeded to not only play the ball from a thirty-foot high branch—which he miraculously landed feet from the front edge of the green—but went on to play every devoured golf ball of his from the past twenty years. It took the *Red Passage* director two weeks to complete the 15th as he insisted on consultation from his former caddy by way of back-and-forth correspondences. One such letter follows:

Dear Cosmo,

I hope you and Mrs. I Told You So are once again playing nicely. I typically side unequivocally with you, old friend, but I must admit, your wife was wise to advise against that little lollipop shrub venture of yours. I heard it was quite the blunder. Though I love the thought of a candy-yielding hedge, I imagine confectionery cultivation to be more a sour enterprise. In your honor, I've penned a character for screen with similar aspirations. I'm calling it *Out on a Limb with No Lolly*.

At any rate, I've gotten myself in a bit of a pickle here and could use that keen savvy of yours—a term I use loosely given your latest business endeavors. Remember that second shot on the fifteenth at Myers Creek I lost to that pine coffin; you know, the tall one? I realize that's a broad statement, as there have been many. These days, I've all but scratched out the existence of this unnerving hole altogether and will, in all likelihood, excuse myself entirely from this suspect leisurely pastime. I was playing a Royal Zipline ball, number 2—my first and last time using that particular make. Well, I took my third from a pinecone and have landed seventy-five yards out in the right rough. At the time of writing, the wind is calm, and we're looking at a back-left pin just off the apron. Though I don't know if that will remain the case for much longer as it's getting dark and the superintendent is bringing out the hole cutter. Please send counsel immediately by way of airmail.

Cordially,

Sammy

P.S. Expect separate correspondence chains in reference to other rounds.

Hole #16 - Harrier Eagle

The magical Myers Creek Perch concludes with one of the most admired and awe-inspiring holes in golf. Named one of the seven wonders of the sporting world by noted columnist Dick Kimball, Harrier Eagle is a 100-yard par three that offers a breathtaking vista of Virginia's arresting scenic beauty. Not to mention, in winter, a glimpse through the bedroom window of Myers Creek resident and supermodel centerfold Eve Lombardo—a sight most say is just as immobilizing. Poet Ernest Young once described the view in fall as "a burning, rich autumnscape of Mother Earth's supple and weakening brilliance." Additionally, in 1958, an oil painting of the iconic hole by renowned impressionist Easton Noel was introduced to the Virginia Governor's Mansion by Governor Hubert Hazel III at the request of his wife as part of their tradeoff for taking down the statesman's beloved singing moose head, tastefully accented with bras hanging from the antlers. The famed 16th at Myers Creek was even featured on a U.S. postage stamp, as well as a Virginia state commemorative coin.

Enraptured by its majesty, first-timers are often unaware of Harrier Eagle's difficulty, to say nothing of its formidable complexity. Although it's one of the shortest par threes on tour, its high-swirling winds and near-blind target make it one of golf's most challenging endeavors—not unlike finding a decent hotel room during championship weekend, or at the absolute least, one with a self-serving waffle iron and easy access to the freeway. Its green sits roughly fifty feet below the tee and is surrounded by fully grown pine trees, with the serene, sometimes swift, Myers Creek running along its front and right sides before flowing toward the old Applebaum Waterwheel. Expanding on the grandeur and tranquility of Harrier Eagle, from time to time, golfers are treated to the heavenly call of a rare, maroon-dipped titmouse—or the cackle of a plastered hillbilly floating down the creek in an inner tube.

In 1963, President John F. Kennedy was iconically photographed sitting on the Carmine Bench at the 16th tee with former British Prime Minister Harold Macmillan whispering an amusing anecdote in his ear. Despite the fact the subject of the witty conservative's pun remains a mystery, it is Jack's gaping laughter that makes the photograph such a heartwarming and humorous moment captured in time. Although, some would argue a more priceless photo of the 35th president was snapped while the then Massachusetts senator was playing in a Cape Cod charity polo match and mistakenly supplied with a Shetland pony.

Hole #17 - Yellow-Throated Kingfisher

This picturesque par four is a slight dogleg right, with Myers Creek running alongside its tee boxes before cutting across the fairway. It's a charming and colorful hole of moderate difficulty with a delightfully woodsy essence—chiefly due to the fact that Yellow-Throated Kingfisher lies on the Myers Creek property line and is mostly isolated from the other holes. It's arguably one of the most peaceful stretches on the entire course and is home to an abundance of curious wildlife, especially the bizarre and fabled three-headed groundhog, which has been sighted an untold number of times by golfers nearing the end of their day's beverage supply. Most have described the beast as a normal-looking groundhog with a head that won't stay in one place.

In 1996, during the Sally Walker Insurance Invitational, acclaimed South African Women's Champion Stacey McCarthy fell victim to a pesky, bushy-tailed squirrel when it snatched her golf ball from the fairway. With the entire golfing community glued to their television sets, this ridiculous "lighter side of sports moment" took an interesting turn when the irksome critter washed its playable plunder in the creek and tried splitting it with a brook trout. On-hand commentators remarked with certainty that the fish appeared to enjoy the resin snack but were divided on the notion that the trout felt the same enthusiasm for its dining partner. Nevertheless, the squirrel and fish were soon joined by an inquisitive garter snake, who—after receiving its own nibble of the tournament leader's ball—decided it wanted the whole thing for itself but just needed a moment to get it all down.

Alas, after a half-hour of trying and several commercial breaks, the garter snake gave up and exited the scene. At the time, one of the on-air analysts offered his interpretation of the snake's actions with a silly cartoonish voice.

"'I could eat it,' I'm sure he said," said the commentator. "'I just don't want to; I-I-I had a Titleist for breakfast.'"

Television viewers later remarked on the former pro's attempt at humor, saying it wasn't bad but felt he missed a perfect opportunity for S-heavy pronunciation. All the same, the squirrel and fish finished the tasty treat themselves, before going their separate ways without even exchanging numbers.

Afterward, McCarthy called over a tournament official to get a ruling on the matter. The official turned to the defending champion and informed her that Rule 18-1, Article C states that if a player's ball is moved, stolen, or eaten by an outside agent or agency—not including caddies—the same ball or a different ball must be replaced at the point where it was manipulated. Unless two or more agencies consumed said ball, in which case, the agencies in question are protected under the United States Fish and Wildlife Service and are therefore entitled to ownership of the ball under consideration. Consequently, concerning the Department of the Interior, Title 50, Part 14(L) of the Code of Federal Regulations, under the heading "Finders Keepers," states that any foreign force willingly introduced into an organism's habitat that is then collectively adopted by the ruling majority of that habitat is thus the property of the said community and as a result, subject to a vote.

After the tournament resumed play, Stacey McCarthy was penalized a stroke for the lost ball and forced to pay a five thousand dollar fine to the federal government.

Hole #18 - Marigold Hummingbird

Eighteen holes at Myers Creek concludes with a thrilling 370-yard slightly uphill par four fondly dubbed Marigold Hummingbird. With a grand view of the clubhouse and the iconic Pinkerton Bridge, and the highly ornate and greatly adored Myers Creek bird hotel situated behind the 18th green, there remains no grander stage in golf for a Sunday afternoon tournament finish. Whether it's a final hole grind—or a leisurely walk to victory several shots ahead of the rest of the field while gesturing gracefully with an outstretched tongue and a thumb to the nose with a waggle of the fingers—Marigold Hummingbird is the picture-perfect ending to not only the most revered course ever constructed but also the sport's most prestigious and sought-after title—the Myers Creek Champion's Tournament.

Comprised of a hundred years of unrivaled tournament history—which includes the savage 1949 18th hole golf club swordplay between final pairing Irwin Fielding and William M. Fiske after a catty comment regarding Fielding's toupee when it blew off the former champion's head and was mistaken for his divot—the winner of the annual Champion's Tournament is awarded the club's highly coveted seersucker jacket. Originally made from fleece and wool in 1922 by accomplished Italian designer Tulio Bianchi, this far from fashionable green and white trophy is without question the sport's highest achievement. As a result, its effect has been known to cause the most composed of athletes to blubber with joy and rethink most of their existing love affairs. Switched to a polyester blend in 1975, with the Myers Creek logo handcrafted to the breast pocket and a coupon for a 2-for-1 steak dinner slipped into the inside pocket, the enviable blazer is customed-fitted, tailored specifically for the victor.

In 1976, after winning the 51st annual Champion's Tournament, golfer Willie Popwell found himself on the unfortunate end of a club faux pas after a disastrous misinterpretation of inches and yards. While television cameras broadcasted out to the airways, with thousands of spectators gathering the 18th green under the bird hotel, the trophy ceremony and much-anticipated jacket presentation reached its rousing yet questionable pinnacle when Chairman Nelson Roloff Jr. presented the newly crowned champion an eleven inch long green and white striped blazer. Swept up in the pageantry, the unknowing chairman—with a big smile for the cameras—spent a half-hour trying to fit Popwell with the doll-sized jacket before sliding it over the champion's hand like a puppet. With a fusillade of camera flashes and rapid firing shutters, Popwell—with his raised blazer all but missing a set of googly eyes and yellow yarn for hair—struck a triumph pose as he lifted the Champion's Tournament Cup. Photos of the touching moment were featured on the front pages of practically every Monday morning newspaper and national sports journal, as well as on the covers of several major craft and hobby periodicals, including *The Puppet Glossy* and *Tiny Tailors Monthly.*

The Fake Food Emporium

*A*re you a business owner in the market for model food? Need a bit of everything but find ordering from catalogs too impersonal? Fed up with over-glossing and price gouging on all your favorites? Then say no to those other fake food suppliers and come on down to The Fake Food Emporium, where we house all your fake food needs under one roof. We've got cheesecake, strawberries, chicken drumsticks, spaghetti and meatballs, even ice! Located in the heart of the city's model food district, you can circle the globe without even leaving the warehouse. Can't find a decent fake cantaloupe? We've got melons that'll blow your mind—pears, pomegranates, passion fruit, and papayas. Our award-winning produce has been featured in grocery chains and buffet decor all across the country. Take a gander at them tomatoes...Ohhh, boy! Carrots? Cucumbers? Cauliflower?! Why, you can literally see the country freshness. Check out those rutabagas! Is this watercress engineered? Engineered to satisfy!

Need fake noodles? Udon? Soba? How 'bout a fried pork cutlet with curry sauce? Then don't forget to venture through our Far East department! We've got over a hundred different pieces of sushi to choose from! Rolls? Sashimi? The other one?! Mix and match if you'd like. We won't tell! Discretion is our middle name. Actually, it's "Services by," but that's just for tax purposes! Lure in customers with tempting window displays. Tantalize their taste buds with model fare so mouthwatering they'll swear to their creator it was real. Tear down those sun-faded photos of who-knows-what and get 'em clamorin' for what's in the window!

Producing a fifty-year-old game show for broadcast television? Liven up your giveaways with scrumptious delights! How much for that big, beautiful grill? Who cares?! Check out those corn cobs! Are those chicken kabobs? Actually, they're soy! Huuuuuuh?! Made from real synthetic plastic polymers, our fake foods have been hand-picked by a team of expert shoppers, who deal exclusively with the finest fake food craftsmen and women alive today...Jeffery Keel, Madalyn Westmore, Django Pugsley...Why I could keep saying names all day!

Realize your dream of opening an upscale 90s restaurant complete with calligraphy and dessert cart. Arm your staff with confidence by sending them out onto the floor with these delectable beauties...apple pie ala mode...red velvet...shortcake! Wheel your way straight into their pleasure centers without those wordy menus. Take 'em on a moonlit rendezvous through the clouds with this flight of fake gelato. Mmmm…different colors!

Got a pastry shop on a desolate downtown thoroughfare? Thought there'd be more foot traffic? Then make that occasional out-of-towner count with heavenly slices of fake black forest in your window. Keen on carrot cake? Coconut? Coffee? Wait a minute…Are those cupcakes topped with bacon? Do you know any other kind, you fat bastard?!

Dabbling in real estate until your candle business takes off? Check out our savory centerpieces and festive cornucopias? Close the deal with a fake turkey so juicy looking your prospects will salivate at the sight. Can't find a towel? No problem! Our fake foods are treated with a water-resistant sealant, so they're non-absorbent! Saliva? Blood? Don't sweat! But if you do, it's OK! Throw all five of the major bodily fluids at any of our fake foods and watch them bead and repel. Go ahead, give 'em a whirl! We won't peek! Are ya doin' it yet?

Give your tours a Thanksgiving scene so ideal *Better Homes and Gardens* will call bullshit. And they'd be right to! Will we fake retaliate with a defamation campaign to make some real cheddar?! Probably!

Own a family furniture store you were guilted into running? Dress up your showroom tabletops with these individually wrapped fake candies…Butterscotch? Cinnamon? Blue?! "Hey, are these orange slices real?" Real fake! "What about this red wine?" You, again?! Let's keep it movin', Twenty-One Questions! Finally, unload that ten-person, triangle-shaped dining room table with these plates of Maine lobster! Animate your patio furniture with breakfast croissants and fake blueberries! Write up a ticket after titillating their fancies with this intimate nighttime scene of bedside chocolates. "Maybe just one more." Wait a minute, I thought you said you had a headache?! Helen? Helen??

Looking for something bigger? Head on over to our bulks department and find all your large-scale fake food needs in scores. It's a plethora of phony porterhouses, briskets, bone-in legs, even crown roasts with decorative frills. Ever seen a fake ham this plump?! Once— but I don't like to talk about it! Pull your car around back so we can load up this big, beautiful replica side of beef. String it up and knock it around if you want. It's your beef!

On a budget?! We've got ya covered! Peruse last year's models inside our discount bargain bins. Waffles? Tacos? Chicken nuggets?! Dig your way to savings through year-old model grub that will last a lifetime. This may be 2017's butter, but it glistens with 2018 luster! Whoever said shopping for fake foods had to break the bank? I don't know!

Stocking up on fake sandwich fixings? Let your imaginations run wild with our fake deli meats! Turkey? Pastrami? Corned beef? Pimento loaf?! Now I've seen everything! Pile 'em high with fake favorites like both kinds of cheese! Lettuce and tomato! Even onions! Plop on a pickle or two. They're plastic! And don't forget to drown your creations with these hand-crafted slices of mayonnaise and mustard. No dollops here! Fake hamburgers?! Don't get me started! Fake hot dogs? Yes, please! Fake french fries? Merci! Popcorn? Donuts? It's fake everything at the Fake Food Emporium!

When my grandfather opened this store in 1958 after sharing a flight to Dallas with a man in nutrition education, he set out to accomplish two things: First, to trick poor people for laughs; and second, to offer quality fake food options for illiterate restaurateurs. And sixty years later, we're still going strong!

Take a trip to Tuscany with this artificial trio…Pesto? Primavera? Bolognese? Look at those sauces shimmer! Got some extra time before your hair appointment? Kids are in the car waiting with the windows rolled up? Tour our very own Pizza Zone and experience fake toppings galore, you neglectful monster! Pepperoni…olives…sardines…and the rest of the classics! Anything goes in this pizza parlor of the mind. Goat cheese? Summer squash? Peas?! Ooookaay!

Take advantage of our loyal shopper program. Buy eleven fake eggs and get the twelfth half off! Enroll your children in our in-house sculpting and molding courses. Don't forget to sign up today for our monthly mailer, with details on next month's trip to the Artificial Food Museum. We'll meet in a parking lot! Fill out these info cards at checkout and enter to win a year's supply of fakes foods based on a national average!

Make wax a thing of the past and demand a standard of excellence from your fake food supplier. Because, like your customers, you're worth it!

Here at the Fake Food Emporium, we offer only the best. But don't just take it from me. Let our satisfied customers do the talking. Like this one! Here's another photo! Check out this happy couple. There's nothing fake about those smiles!

Voted 2016 Best Fake Bento Box by *Replica Cuisine Magazine*, here at the Emporium, we stand behind all our fake foods. That's why we offer a one hundred percent money-back guarantee on all non-digested products. Semi-digested? Would ya settle for store credit? Of course, you would! It's our policy!

So, what are you waiting for?! Get yourselves down to the Fake Food Emporium, where the food is fake, and the savings are real! Have ya left yet? Can't find your keys?! Don't fret! Just retrace your steps! On the phone when you got in last night? Had to go to the bathroom real bad? Called the restaurant, but they don't open until five? Check your front door! They are?! You're lucky to be alive, stupid! Now make your way over to The Fake Food Emporium at the corner of Chester and Whaley! Remember…"Real store, fake foods!"

One-Star Genius

*A*cclaimed theologian, mythologist, and philosopher Robert Young recently found himself the subject of academic intrigue following the latest publication from literature professor and Young scholar Maxwell Stein—whose work offers fresh knowledge and insight into the mind of the prolific writer through a comprehensive study of Young's online customer reviews. With a thick tapestry of lectures and writings on topics ranging from religious origin stories to modern social constructs, Young's ability to articulate and simplify the most complex of philosophies and theories into easily digestible content, without sacrificing emphasis, is communicated brilliantly in this review for an automated cat feeder:

DO NOT BUY!!! ONE-STAR!!!

Young's brief yet concise declaration, coupled with his use of all caps and multiple exclamation points, solidifies the author's dissatisfaction with and disdain for the YummyPet Programmable Cat Feeder—while at the same time capturing his earnest plea to potential buyers who may be considering the item as a cost-efficient alternative to expensive pet sitters. Members of an industry that at the time of Young's review were under heavy scrutiny for their adoption of the fifty-minute hour, introduced years earlier by 1970s analysts and D.C.-area call girls—prevalent backlash brimming with social commentary, Young's poignant assessment echoes the changing culture. A thorough man and owner of nine cats, two dogs, and an obese hedgehog, the haunted genius waged war for decades against lackluster pet care and was notorious for leaving sitters a three-hundred-page typed document of detailed instructions, including specific scenarios, illustrations, and a list of severe consequences should the requests not be carried out properly. One such ramification resulted in the kitchen pantry locking automatically—and always the one with the good stuff inside. Of heavy irony, displaying the master's wit, this discipline was seen on several occasions by Young's longtime gardener, who remained faithful to the wishes of *The Power of Symbiotics* author. Except for one time when he planted buttercups instead of roses and lied about it without even flinching—a period Stein refers to, in his second Young publication, as the "icy summer."

This review for the Cako 3-Piece Paring Knife Set

BUYER BEWARE!! Cheap material, useless serrations, and handle. Not to mention the 2-½ inch bird's beak knife is hooked more like a talon than a beak. SHAME!!!

comes as a great shock, both in its verbose language and chastising tone. Posted after spending several months in the bush living with the indigenous peoples of Naru, a small island off the coast of Tasmania, separated from modern conveniences and gourmet cutlery, Young's fascination for the tribe's primitive yet ingenious ways of life— romanticized in his book *Myths and the Human Psyche in the Modern World*—expresses the author's difficult transition back into advanced society. Young's use of the word "useless" to describe the serrated edges and handles is particularly interesting in that it supports longstanding theories that the celebrated writer is, in fact, an ambidextrous chef. Meaning when cooking, he favors his left hand. A belief born of Young's writings in Part I of *Ego and the External World*, where he speaks of a person performing daily tasks with their non-dominant appendages to confuse the id and keep things interesting—kicking, snapping, masturbating. This thinking, of course, led to Young's supplemental studies in blood flow and muscular impetus, resulting in his one and only medical essay, "Mythologized Science and the Body," offering, at length, wisdom on the benefits of numb appendages—which Young referred to as "phantom touch"—as well as exercises and techniques for achieving full range of motion with the human tongue through total consciousness. Young's incorporation of his opposite hand to peel, chop, and dice would find the right-handed knives of Cako Cutlers and the offset concaves of the handles most frustrating and quite "useless," even for the most self-aware, cross-dominant cook. The distinction between talon and beak, compelling and highly revealing, reflects Young's fondness for birds and birdwatching. A known recluse, Young lives on an island in Washington state, accessible only by ferry. His passion for ornithology—found predominantly in this review of the 13-inch, green matted Audobon Singing Bird Clock (retail price: $29.99 + $5.99 for shipping)

Worst clock ever!!! Would give it zero stars if I could. Arrived late and without batteries. And to add insult to injury, the call of the Yellow-Breasted Warbler is, in fact, the wrong variety. One would imagine that the knowledgeable folks over at the QUOTE society UNQUOTE—a term I now use loosely and more often in the presence of sheep and other wooly ruminants with a herd mentality—would know the difference between a Blue-Throated Warbler and a Yellow-Breasted Warbler. What is this? Freakin' amateur hour?! Come on!!

purchased on August 2, 2015—offers students and scholars alike a window into the philosopher's tortured soul. The tension, sternness, and unapologetic nature of the "Audobon Review" can be traced back to Young's time on Madison Avenue when he served as the senior brand consultant and head of marketing psychology for the Samuel & Willis Co. (ad agency). A period of Young's life often excluded from his writings due entirely to the author's crippling guilt and lingering self-condemnation—efforts, Young once, in a television appearance, equated to "murder" and categorized as "rudimentary manipulation."

An assertion he described as "playing the human heart as routinely as a Sunday morning pipe organ."

Profits soared under Young's compartmentalizing of customers and their desires, changing the face of advertising and reinforcing Western aesthetics in marketing. In *A Conscious Life*, Stein quotes Young from his interview with public radio personality Christopher Keelan, transcribed in the book *Conversations with Robert Young*: "Man's exploit of the aspirations and fancies of his fellow man is a vileness tantamount to crimes against humanity. To prey and profit on the desperation and disillusionment of man's plight and the human condition using a standard of culturally assigned desires with implied guarantees of success and happiness to control and push product is pure evil. Are there any croissants left?" Young's trolling of the famed avian non-profit, calling into question the status of their organization, although humorous, demonstrates the distinguished author's persistent pain in the form of a publicly adverse response—the emotional and mental suffering brought on by his role in modern commercialism, perpetuated by the window displays and glass cases of Madison Avenue. A conviction present throughout Young's work, supported by Stein's recent examinations, it appears the undisputed grandfather of myths and symbols has been all but consumed by the very thing he sought to expose. It is this internal struggle that provided Young with his iconic and often repeated truism: "That's a pretty hat, but you're still going to die."

Moreover, this review for a set of towels

Disappointed and dejected. 1-½ stars. The once youthful radiance of the Molvena Ultra-Soft, Low-Lint Hand Towels (Color: Daffodil) bears years of wear after only several washes. Abraded by dry skin and psoriasis. Ebbed away and frayed. Faded of pigment. Reduced to a rag suitable for gunk and grime and cheap polishes. A once shining testament to Turkish cotton and woven borders, gracing my antique brass FlexMount towel bar—which I purchased specifically for these hand towels—now lay wadded in a grocery bag under the kitchen sink. Forgotten. Passed over for a younger hand towel with flashy pinstripes and a phallic-shaped automobile with tickets to the Met in the glove compartment because I don't like Wagner—HE'S A POMPOUS HACK! Goddamn, that makes me mad!

is reflective of Young's compounded anguish and forlorn spirit, which plagued the elder architect during his collective works in *Death Myths and Sweet Release*. The apparent parallel drawn between the hand towels and Young himself is not only indicative of his later reviews— not unlike the 2011 KitchenWorks.com review where Young made a strikingly poetic comparison between the Marvel 2-Speed 200-Watt Hand Blender and his libido—but also provides additional insight into the estranged relationship with his third wife, Karen Jacobs, who left him for a younger man. At the time of their marriage, Young was thirty years her senior, and even though they connected on an intellectual level, his proverbial sword—as it's analogized in Young's medieval theme of the knight whose blade is of a weaker grade and considerably skinner—in his golden age, was rarely up for battle. And no matter how many tongue reps he totaled each day, a distance grew between him and his wife. Furthermore, his wife and her new lover shared an adoration for structurally lavish composers with an ear for the musically bombastic and often dull. In a letter to his ex-wife, Young compared her and her lover's affection for irritating and exhausting composers with embellished and uninspired tendencies to a Millennial's wine palate, with selections under fifteen dollars and paired with the films of Baz Luhrmann.

Finally, the review for this pair of nut-brown, 30-inch-long shoelaces

sucks

seems to be Young's most telling assessment on offer inside this fascinating publication. Unabridged and without punctuation—a byproduct of his extensive studies in *Punctuation and the Super-Ego*, as well as the revisited and updated edition, *Punctuation, Emojis, and the Super-Ego*, which insists the presence of a contemporary social bias toward punctuation and its strain on self-image—the "Shoelaces Review" displays both a return to a succinct use of language and his understanding of the totality of the human consciousness as it attempts to flourish in a systematic world. That is one of predetermined beliefs based in a particular time and region—the experience. And out of this, the birth of an authentic life that possesses a spontaneous nature, unmolested by presumptions and expectations.

Of true values, pure and unwavering in the face of morality. The recruiting of others that share the new archetype's unfettered nature and desire for change. The science of thought and the conception of an idea, which then leads to a revolution. The introduction of the character's half-brother—a bastard—and the realization that you are that bastard. Unauthentic and toeing the line. A coward, incapable of change. The acceptance of your role and the devastation endured at length until the bitter end. The coming to grips with the recognition that you are, in short, subpar shoelaces, and the universe does not care about you. The "Sucks Phenomenon," as Young so eloquently expounded on in *Choice, Fears, and Better Luck Next Time.*

The Frasier Lawns Croquet Tournament

*T*he Frasier Lawns Croquet Tournament kicks off today, and anybody who's anybody knows that this posh affair is not only a celebrated display of pure, unbridled athleticism equivalent to that of the Roman gladiators or the Greeks at Olympia but is also a perfect place for picking up women. Now, I don't mean your everyday, run-of-the-mill dames; I'm talking sophisticated, well-bred ladies—women of class and status. Not to mention, and most importantly, filthy rich. Myself being a man of very little means and dwindling prospects, I've developed over the years a hankering for the good life. Why, as far back as my last bounced check for four dollars and thirty-three cents, of which I purchased a secondhand beach towel and a fish taco from a place called Salty's, it has been my aspiration to live on easy street. I don't necessarily need to own property on said street; in fact, I'd settle for a sublet. Right now, it's a hell of a commute, and I haven't any change for parking. Now, of course, I would never go to one of these things without first doing my homework.

Thumbing through the quotes and a number of financial biweeklies, it seems this year's guest list will be a fruitful and auspicious one. So, I see it only appropriate that I don my whites and polish my mallet and begin forging my invitation.

Firstly, there is Ms. Rebecca Tisdale, a skinny little creature, meek and fair skin, nothing really to write home about—then again, if one felt inclined and had the stationary, something could perhaps be penned to the neighbors instead. She stands by the club's famed oak tree in an unassuming white eyelet dress with lemonade in hand, exuding a quality of aloof pride that repels even the mosquitoes. Luckily, where her Rocky Mountain peaks fall flatter than the plains of Nebraska, one will surely find a kind heart and a generous checkbook—a combination that has her name springing from my lips with boyish glee. She comes from the South, where her family made their fortune in the peach smuggling business. In the forties, her father transported bushels of illegal, Georgia-grown peaches across state lines during the postwar tomato-peach feud, which pitted southern against southern in a dispute between vitamin A and C. Tennesseans lived by the tomato seed but craved the forbidden nectar, and the Tisdale Empire grew.

Growers feared the name and the man behind it. Her father became a legend, the figure of countless spook stories future tomato growers undoubtedly heard about in school. While back on Georgia soil, his name was spoken equally to that of a hero. "Hombre con un sueno," or "man with a dream," rang from the hearts of the poor orchard workers. Though like with all good organizations, the mesocarp had to hit the fan eventually, and for the Tisdale crime family, such a collapse came sooner than later with the drought of '59. Lord Tisdale was arrested at the Buckshot Diner, where he was found eating, of all sandwiches, a B.L.T. Before his trial and conviction, Mr. Tisdale placed his funds into an offshore account guarded by a series of large coconut trees and a surprisingly smart bird with an unusual liking for french fries. Dreaming of this bounty of unaccounted for wealth, I can't help but see the acid-tongued Ms. Rebecca Tisdale as a strong candidate.

Standing by the buffet, discreetly hoovering a wedge of white cake, is Ms. Abigail Plum—a jolly sort whose hunger for life and caramelized nuts fills a body with ageless vigor and vitality and a fear of wearing shoes with an open toe. She's the kind of girl that makes you question the integrity of your patio furniture; the kind of sweet and mild-mannered beauty that makes a union with her seem simply enchanting and extremely uncomfortable—especially in a broom closet; the kind of girl that keeps you smiling from sunup to sundown and has you rethinking measurements when preparing a dinner for two. She's an insatiable woman whose girth and appetite are conceded only to the size of her bank account, making her a true contender for receiving my love. Her money is old (the best kind) and began with her grandfather's investments in the timber industry with the founding of the Plum Toothpick Company. The proud son of Washington's Okie Ridge, Harvey Randolph Plum created a multinational brand dedicated to the extraction of left behind food particles. An ironic thought given the unsightly spectacle that is his granddaughter moments after meeting a tray of deviled eggs or lemon custard puffs.

The sporty yet stately woman on the featured center court, graciously mopping the floor with a group of portly men in Bermuda length shorts—who appear none too happy with the fact they're losing to a woman, but who seem rather happy about the shorts—is Marion von Klaus. A member of the von Klaus royal family and first daughter of the Monarch of Amsforth, this noble and self-assured maiden possesses not only a mouthwatering hoard of ancestral jewelry—some of which adorn a hand the likes of which every man would kiss and tell—but also an unquenchable thirst for adventure.

At the age of nineteen, she became the first female to fly a solo hot air balloon from Frankfort to Hamburg. When asked why Hamburg, she replied, "Because I ran out of relish." At age twenty, she won the Maldonado Rally, a prestigious auto race along the African coast of the Mediterranean. The other racers rolled into the finishing city of Carlo-Ville four hours later to the sight of Ms. von Klaus sitting at a course-side café slurping champagne with a mouthful of oysters, recapping the race to a swarm of journalists. An avid hunter and gameswoman (a term she coined in the inaugural issue of *Outdoor Feminist*), the name Marion von Klaus is held in high regard within the sporting community. She was the first person to track down and document the legendary red-haired yak of southern Mongolia's Annaburro mountain range. She lived among the beasts of the snow-capped hills and survived on cumin salads and ginger ice. During the annual Wellington Meadows Golf Tournament, she shot a Saturday round of 59, and later that evening, during a spirited game of nine-ball, won Edmond Lauder's treasured racehorse Don't Skimp on the Mustard. Due to the fumigation taking place in the billiard room, the match transpired in the resort's Murray Hall during the dinner service, where Mr. Liam Marlow received a nasty bruise on his forehead thanks to a runaway cantaloupe that stood in for the eight ball. Princess von Klaus took victory when she pocketed Sir Hugo Loughton's chocolate cream pie into his wife's lap. She once swam the Barabay Channel in the middle of springtime during the blue suckerfish mating season. When she reached the Dansworth Banks, her toes were so swollen she had to be carried out of the water and was forced to wear thong sandals for the remainder of the year—which made quite the scene at the royal wedding of Prince Albert, Duke of Eaton and Lady Elizabeth.

The mere thought of trying to keep up with such an expansive and worldly woman is enough to send most inexperienced men packing. Fortunately, I've found that love trumps exhaustion, and one doesn't utter the word adversity when dealing with a woman worth more than a small country—or at the very least a province with a seat at the Assembly of Nations, or its own table at Lily's Pancake House.

The shapely woman with curves both north and south, standing by the shade tents, is Ms. Maxine Hardwicke, a loveable, cockeyed beauty who's slow on the uptake and quick on the champagne. This mixture of indiscretion and unladylike conduct, though rousing and presenting a want for Polaroids, has built a certain reputation for the prominent daytime game show model. A reputation that, when paired with a heap of accumulated wealth in the form of taxable prizes and exotic giveaways, one can't help but wonder what's behind door number three.

And though her attic light flickers dimly, her benevolent nature more than makes up for it—a helpful trait I'm sure to exploit while presenting myself as a prince or ambassador from some faraway land plagued with pestilence and famine and no decent sports teams. Her television personality makes her a true front-runner in my decision as I've always wanted to see my name amidst the society pages. Especially the gossip column of Ida Miller; she spins a tale the likes of which nobody can hold a candle to—unless it's burned at both ends. Ms. Hardwicke's celebrity, though wavering at times, has made her a kissable cash cow of endorsements and royalties, a steady flow of funds that will surely provide for us both until we're old and grey and suffering from a lack of buoyancy.

One of the finest examples of cold-hearted indifference among the club's gentry is Ms. Libby Mayweather, a stoic dish with bland expression and a sophisticated proficiency in gold-digging—a talent she's perfected over the years of love and loss and laced gin glasses. She sits on a bench by the lawn's long-revered Alice Pond, legs crossed, mingling with a group of interested and unsuspecting elderly gentlemen, weaving a web of seduction and the promise of handcuffs.

She paralyzes her prey with intellect and charm, and, more effectively, talks of her new strapless brassiere and how it works on the same principles as a netted-beach ball caddy. To go to bed with this woman would mean certain death or alimony—both of which I've been advised by my legal counsel to avoid.

Nevertheless, her vast swell of bequeathed assets is too tantalizing a prospect to simply ignore, even though a life with her may mean no life at all. It's a chance one must take in this situation. After all, it's high time I get over this inane hang-up regarding life and my own extinction. Then again, with town squares adorning gold statues of me generously depicted in a victorious pose, who needs immortality? She's a willful and determined woman with a track record to prove it. Why, if one wandered down Melody Lane, they would surely find her signature spider hairclips on the nightstands of every eligible bachelor over seventy with an amassed fortune and a terrible heart condition.

There was Joseph L.B. Tate, a notable hotel giant with assets aplenty, mainly local and centralizing around his midriff. An unusually brisk character, full of good humor and malted candies, the late Mr. Tate passed down the fruits of his labor to Libby, his young new wife, after finally succumbing to a thirty-year battle with an uncontrollable lust for giblets in bed. Then, there was the Diary King, Samuel Littlefield, founder of the Littlefield Dairy Farms and owner of the world's first buttermilk bath, which he soaked in each evening before bed. Unfortunately, this nightly regimen made Mr. Littlefield susceptible to bad dreams, and one evening, he took a tongue-lashing from ten thousand blue kittens while on Candycane Lane. Lastly,

Walter Birch, the well-though-of southern gothic novelist from Mississippi, whose celebrated works include *Madam Ruby's Midnight Summon* and *The Alligator Tango*.

And finally, one mustn't forget the unobtrusive and recently accepted figure within the Frasier Lawns elite, Miss Rose Liebowitz, a shy and modest number with mousy features and a strip mall perm— a girl whose mere existence is news to most. Luckily, I subscribe to a variety of papers, big and small, and have a particular fondness for page four. She loiters by the service entrance with considerable trepidation, planting herself behind a series of potted palms and a large sweatered-man whose build resembles that of a deep freeze.

A classic fish out of water scenario, Miss Liebowitz's riches are new to the scene and came to her courtesy of a grocery store sweepstakes put on by the Diamond Dixie Supermarket chain in conjunction with MayCare Foods. Her task was simple: Redeem the most coupons at any participating Diamond Dixie store during the current year. Her victory of twenty thousand plus coupons came easy with the help of the *Daily Saver* and a weekly misplaced buddle of *Discount Shopper*'s thanks to the willing grace of a fancying postman. She was given the title "American Coupon Queen" and awarded a small fortune and groceries for life.

Like a weed among flowers, Miss Liebowitz innocently announces her arrival to high society by making nervous chit-chat: Firstly, with a member of the club's kitchen staff; then with herself; and finally, with a half-eaten turkey sandwich. To unveil this timid beauty's true appeal, one must look past her sad and objectionable uncertainty—which she unsuccessfully attempts to mask with a sort-of periodic swinging of her arms, the occasional bounce of her shoulders, and an ungodly number of references to the state of Maryland—and focus on the intact and unpolluted prosperity that arrives each month to her mailbox in the form of a small corporately cut check. A seemingly futile conquest given the aforementioned list of flush women brimming with cash and the will to spend it, but then again, green is green, and when it's coupled with naivety, it seems that much sweeter.

Of course, I would probably have to settle for a townhouse downtown and give up my dream of a house in the country. A sacrifice I wanted to avoid but would be willing to make. That is if the help was live-in, and the master bath was big enough for a collection of harps—a hobby I'll undoubtedly start after the arrival of the ostrich rugs.

A Dish Best Served Cold
and with a Basket of Fries

*I*t was twenty-five years ago this month that the now-famous *November 1992 issue of Restaurateur Magazine published with much regret the dissolve of the legendary and long-running business partnership of Erwin and Stan Flynn. The respective brothers were co-founders of the cherished Northern California drive-in Flynn's, which received national prestige when it was first included on Hoffman's list of the Top 10 Burger Joints in the country. Its fame grew exponentially in 1972 when it served as the central hangout and filming location for the classic coming-of-age summer comedy Out-of-School and Horny, written and directed by American Fancy alumnus Calvin Ruckus. After disbanding, Erwin continued the Flynn family tradition at its popular location, 800 College Avenue in Santa Rosa, while his younger brother, Stan, opened his own drive-in restaurant across the street, taking with him an ample portion of the newly named Original Flynn's clientele. In honor of the anniversary of*

A Dish Best Served Cold and with a Basket of Fries

what famed food journalist, Janet Bell, called "The Day Curbside Died," Restaurateur Magazine has published the following, previously undisclosed, series of correspondences between the two brothers in the wake of their fabled separation:

Dear Erwin,

    I felt I should take a moment and pen you a letter given the events of the last several months. I want you to know that my decision to open Stanley's was purely out of a need to challenge myself and was in no way a reflection on the business or our relationship. I have nothing but love for you. You're my older brother, and you have always been there for me. When pop was sick and wanted to take that cruise and all my money was tied up in the new condo, it was you that showed me those affordable packages. When Marie was leaving and trying to take Collin away, it was you that remained stoic with a display of staunch impartiality by serving as Marie's character witness. A fairness unpossessed by most men. And it was you that fed Maxine and the goldfish last August during my stay at the clinic, even though most of the fish lost their scales and Maxie now growls at me when I cry. I wouldn't be where I am today if it weren't for your guidance and devotion throughout these many years. I owe every bit of my past and future successes to you. You are my brother, my mentor, and my best friend. And I will always love you and hold you in the highest regard.

Always,

Stan

Dear Stan,

Your letter brought me to tears. You truly are a wonderful human being filled with nothing but good. Your concern for others, be it family or strangers off the street, is one of your most remarkable and admirable qualities. I am honored and humbled to be your brother. And as your brother and former partner, it has been my privilege to watch you grow into the smart, business-savvy man you've become over these many yet very short years. Honestly, I'd be lying if I said you hadn't taught me a few tricks here and there. You've always shown potential and unwavering self-discipline, even at a young age. You would have been fine without me. If anything, I have only hindered you in some way or another up to this point. And for that, I apologize. So, now, let us sever the proverbial ties that have bound you to my old and outdated ways and allow your young wings to spread and soar you to new heights. I have all the faith in the world in you, and I trust your new venture will flourish for years to come. Should you ever need me, though, you know just where to find me.

With love, respect, and admiration,

Erwin

Dear Erwin,

Your faith in me means the world. My entire life, I've sought your approval, and now that I've secured it, I feel a newfound sense of confidence. A confidence I will use to undoubtedly make you proud and, at the same time, breathe new life into the family name. After all, we both know it's gotten a little stale and, dare I say, pompous over the last ten or so years, what with the changes in vendor quality and cutbacks because of the new highway and all those fast-food drive-thru places going up, and the mounting bills and pressure to sell a few more onion rings. Not that I didn't have a blast with you in the back-office night-after-night rolling pennies for payroll. Those were swell times. Stanley's is my opportunity to bring the joy and excitement back into the whole curbside experience. Like the kind of time mom and dad had. Like then, this is a new era. Nobody wants a semi-thawed cardboard patty covered in some kind of yellow cheese. People want gourmet burgers these days. You know? Artisanal. Piled high with healthy and humane-sounding ingredients. Like brioche and rucola. Kale. They don't always have to know what they are, as long as they're unconventional. We'll add these little, charming narratives to the bottom of our new energy-efficient solar menus, telling our customers where their ingredients came from, whether it's a real place or not. It doesn't matter. And that's the important thing. Because we'll cram the copy with words like pasture-raised, local, and in-house. "Old Brook Farms." Sounds like a real place, doesn't it? And we'll stay away from names like "Big Papa" or "Heart Attack," while drastically limiting the number of burgers with the word "The" in front of it. It's always been my dream to sell a burger so choice, so premium that its mere existence creates an entirely new standard on which all subsequent burgers are judged. I'm just so thankful that when this dream becomes a reality next month with our grand opening, I'll have a permanent friend just a stone's throw away. Well, that is, if the rent over there doesn't continue to climb, and you're able to turn a profit with your trays of grease. I'm just giving you a hard time, brother. It's fun to wake up in the middle of the night and feel like your stomach's turned into a nuclear waste facility. Did you get the edible arrangement I sent over?

Faithfully,

Stan

P.S. Really, it would mean a lot to me to have you at the store for the opening. Side by side. Like old times. This is as much yours as it is mine. That said, we're expecting a pretty promising turnout, so I was hoping we could use your lot for overflow. Thanks, brah!

Baby brother,

Your last letter found me in high humor. Your spirit amuses me. I applaud your vision: "A new standard for burgers." That's quite an undertaking. An Everest of a bar, really. Honestly, I hate to be the seasoned veteran here with a long-winded spew of discouragement, peppered with harsh reality checks aimed at crushing your spirit and knocking over that first domino in a series of personal failures—which ultimately cause you to question not only your overall perspective but every natural and seemingly insightful inkling you've ever known—but if you think you're setting that bar with fancy, la-di-da language, you've got a big surprise coming to you. Beef...cheese...onions, lettuce, and tomato—these are the words that resonate with the public. Words they can rely on. Makes them feel all warm inside. Makes them feel American. Kale, my boy, is the transient, drug-addicted stepchild of lettuce and tomato. Shit's mean. Goes down fighting, if it goes down at all. A topping of the times, believe me. You don't think I experimented a little? Oh, I love bacon...with my eggs. Stick to the classics. Then again, don't let me tell you how to run your solar-powered money pit. What are you guys building over there, a burger joint or a spaceship? I hear Martians love all that icky green stuff. I'm just coming from thirty years of experience, that's all. Thirty years comprised of over three hundred newspaper and magazine articles including countless features—one of which, as you know, food critic and diabetes advocate Chuck Harlow called me, not you, the "Burger King of California" (Remember that sting?)—a dozen TV interviews, three documentaries, two class actions, and one settlement. Thirty years of leadership. In the front of house and behind. Actual leadership. Thirty years of tough decisions and dirty work. Tell me, brother...who was it that convinced mom and pop to take an extra day or two a week away from the restaurant? And who convinced pop to step down entirely after mom died so their sons could take over, even though it was all he had to occupy his time? And who put him in a nursing home when he got that smell and made that unmistakable transition old people make where they have more things in their freezer than their fridge? Face it, brother...you rode coattails. So, sure, go right ahead, use my lot if you feel so inclined; after all, we're family. Oh, and as for that beautiful edible arrangement you sent over...the fruit one with the Stanley's T-shirt, size extra-large...what a lovely gesture. You shouldn't have. Unfortunately, it seems someone placed it behind the back wheel of my car, and I backed right over it. Confused, I put the car into drive and drove over it again. Still dazed, I backed over it several more times before inexplicably spinning my tires on it. Probably the handiwork of some hood. I scooped up the pulpy remains with a shovel and returned it to the front step of your establishment in hopes of claiming a new one. And if, for some bizarre reason, it smells of urine, it's most likely from one of the stray dogs I've noticed hanging around your store after hours. Must be after that rancid funk you deem revolutionary. Smells like sour milk and veggie toots enjoying a quick fifteen in the sauna.

Fondly,

Erwin

Brother,

I was very upset to read of the fate of the edible arrangement. It had starfruit. No worries, big bro. I remedied the situation yesterday by sending over a dozen more. Needless to say, I was shocked to hear that someone had replaced the arrangement's contents with a collection of fully developed hornet nests. That's awful. The scene from across the street is clearly one of chaos and panic. I just pray everyone's okay. Probably the work of the same hood. Or one with an identical last name. It makes me wonder how safe the neighborhood really is these days. Well, on your side of the street anyway. What with the promise of future transgressions and all. Not to mention the costs of fumigation. Or maybe just pick up a bottle of spray. If I were you, I'd cut my losses and get out while I still had air in my tires. That said, I noticed a tow truck in your parking lot. Did that same jolly-seeking miscreant slash the tires of your car? What a terrible shame. The good news is you won't accidentally be backing over any more edible arrangements.

With love,

Stan

Dear mistaken afterbirth,

I must apologize for missing your big opening over there at Loose Stools. You see, I spent the last week at First Grace Hospital, where I was being treated for an alarming number of hornet stings. My early treatment consisted of several painful adrenaline injections, which made their way into my already weakened muscles. The venom had coursed its way through my body like a raging river. Much like the river I took you rafting on for your sixteenth birthday. Oh, no, that's right, you didn't go because you were too scared. Instead, you stayed home with mom and canned peaches. You would have been more of a man had you scraped off some of that peach fuzz and glued it to your sack; if only you had one. You ever imagine your wife with that guy she left you for? If I were you, I certainly wouldn't think of them staring into each other's eyes as he enters her and the elation that fills her body. Don't imagine that. That's probably really painful. Their smiles and her telling him how amazing he feels before they build in intensity and violate each other's every orifice. I can't see how dwelling on those minor yet devastating details would be too constructive. But seriously, whatever you do, don't think of her begging for him and pulling him in deep as he finishes. That's not helping anybody—them both wearing a look of afterglow. You don't need that right now. Enjoy your new business, and don't let the images of a strange man that probably knows your wife better than you ever did being inside her and her wanting every drop. And that's the important part—her wanting every drop. Don't fixate on that aspect. Don't let it loop over and over in your head until it ruins you. Don't go back to that place. Don't dig yourself into another depression thinking about their new family and that guy tucking in your son. Focus on your funny, French-sounding condiments. Focus on how the hell you're going to make that work. Don't think about the happiness your once family is feeling now that you're gone.

Respectfully,

Erwin

Mr. Flynn:

How's Julio? Have you promoted him from dishwasher yet? The three of us should really get together soon for a drink. I always liked Julio. Such a hard worker. And loyal. Boy, is that kid loyal. He'd do just about anything for you. Like, give you his social security number to open an account for the restaurant's outstanding utility bills. Oh, that's right, he didn't do that; you did. Now, one must imagine that there's a criminal investigation unit somewhere out there that would love to get their hands on that little nugget. Not to mention the California Department of Revenue regarding that three-year period when our credit card machine was down, and we were "Cash Only." You can't see, but I'm winking. Perhaps, I should draft them a letter and give 'em the inside skinny on Original Flynn's. Honestly, I've been laboring on this notion for some time now. Took it to the park and walked it around the duck pond. I mean, no business can be expected to run successfully with something like that hanging over its head. And then I asked myself...What kind of brother would I be if I didn't help the man who gave me everything? So, I went ahead and wrote those lovely people of the appropriate authorities an anonymous letter. I also attached a list of building violations and hazards I know haven't been dealt with for years—electrical, plumbing, fire. Stuff like that. Not that it really matters; the store will be gone, and you'll be in jail. I know you'd do the same for me, brother. Oh, and while I'm helping, remember to cut with the vein, not across.

See you in hell,

The cuter son

P.S. I get off to those thoughts of my ex-wife. Lesson: You can't break something that's already broken. Enjoy the fall.

Dearest Stan,

By the time you read this letter, I'll be beachside, burying my face in the big, beautiful breasts of an exotic woman who will undoubtedly mistake my American accent for a decent human being. Really, I owe it all to you. What can I say? You liberated me. Sure, at the time, maybe I would have appreciated more of a heads-up. You know, let me get my shit together. But this way worked out! Stopped and got me a whole new wardrobe—a bunch of silk and linen. And you know, made sure they were a couple of sizes too big, so folks know I'm easy-going and ready to make a fool of myself talking to people twenty years younger than me because I'm clinging to the belief that age is irrelevant in the presence of drugs. Even took in a haircut and a shave. I'm a blond now! I tell ya, really, this whole thing is long overdue. I just needed to pack it in, as they say, liquidate as many assets as possible in a frantic afternoon and just move on. There's no time like the present, am I right? You know, it just occurred to me...You haven't been giving yourself enough credit. Sure, I'll admit, I took a few shortcuts and liberties with the restaurant and the identities of our employees. Big brother was doing what needed to be done. That was the role I took on. But, somehow, in all this back and forth, we've failed to touch on your contributions, which we both know far surpass my efforts. Big brother may have gotten his hands dirty, but what does little brother have on his? Interesting question. I'm reminded of years ago, right after pop left...Jared's Mega Burger had just gone in, and we had lost our roller-skating license after Becky face-planted into the side of that conversion van. We were broke and all out of ideas, and it appeared Flynn's was on its last leg. I remember an evening when I was in the back cooking more than just burgers, and Sal Panzini came into the store. I seem to recall a deal you made with him involving a hefty loan you took out without my knowledge and the trouble you had paying it back. I remember the threats he made and the urgency to get to him before he got to you. But most importantly, I remember your fascinating story months later involving a shovel and a hole in the cellar of our family establishment. That restaurant's sitting on more than just a mountain of debt. Must have been a lot to carry around? No wonder Marie split. Oh, remember, it was her lover that did the splitting. And since you helped broaden my perspective, I'd like to return the favor. That's why I drafted a little letter of my own to the Santa Rosa Sheriff's Department. They got this new DNA testing thing. Have you read about this? They can match up literally anything. Anyway, you're about to be a lot more familiar with it than me, that's for sure.

With love and kisses from paradise,

Erwin

Hey brother,

It's been a while. I know a lot's gone down since we last wrote. Hey, can you believe the stuff they're saying about us in the papers? There's no call for that kind of slander. Said they picked you up at a Texas beach resort, coked out of your gourd and rubbing yourself against the furniture in the lobby. Some fall, huh? Sounds like your trial went smoothly, though...five years for eleven counts of fraud and identity theft. Not bad. That half a million in damages might hurt. I wouldn't worry about it. I'm sure you'll bounce back. Listen, even with your old-man ways, you're the cleverest person I know. Time in here's kind of opened my eyes. Anyway, I should get going; I've got my plea hearing in an hour. I think things are going to work out; Panzini was a real piece shit. Anyway, fingers crossed.

Your brother,

Stan

Dearest Stan,

It was wonderful hearing from you! It's great our counselors are letting us write to one another. I hope you're not sore at me, what with turning you in for murder and all. I know what you mean; the time's allowed me to get straight and focus on what really matters— family. I've written a book! *Confessions of a Burger Joint.* It's kind of a tell-all slash recipe book. The sales are through the roof and ought to take care of the damages with plenty left over. Hey, last week, they fed us these burgers with aioli. I'm not even sure how to pronounce it correctly. But you were right, it's delicious. I think. How's about when you and I get out of here, we move up north to Oregon or Washington and give that artisanal approach of yours a shot? The right way. Side by side.

Always,

Erwin

Dear Erwin,

I'll see you in eight to ten, partner.

Stan

Faking One Giant Leap

*I*f you had told me that on the other end of the telephone was the president of the United States asking me, Ruben Merriweather—an over-the-hill, washed-up musical has-been with a big toe sticking out of his sock and several hundred dollars in the hole, thanks to a hasty, ill-informed bet placed against the success of The Beatles in their first year, which I thought was a lock after seeing their hair and having no prior knowledge of them—to not only take part in what was going to be the biggest dupe in universe history but also plan and execute it, I probably would have left the ringing well enough alone.

I was past my prime in every sense of the saying, as I hadn't had a choice cut of beef in eons. Back in my heyday, though, I was so flush with cash I was using filet mignon as paperweights. Downside was whenever I brought my work home, the neighborhood dogs would follow. Ah, those were the days. Sadly, by the time this whole debacle began in '63, I was lucky enough to find myself in front of a bowl of watery refuse. Or gazpacho. There was no difference. And if, on a particularly blessed day, I found myself in His good graces and the recipient of miraculous prosperity, I would be treated to something particularly scrumptious while rummaging through my neighbors' cupboard as they were out to Mass.

I lived on the West Side of Chicago near Antipasto Avenue. The smells alone wafting through the streets provided enough carbohydrates for one man or a group of four aggressively bi-curious boys. Unfortunately, nasal nutriment did nothing to aid in my appetite, as I've been bedeviled by a deviated septum ever since actress Marla Calhoun punched me in the nose after I mistook her Don Loper muff as the results of a relaxed holiday diet. My apartment had a Murphy bed that caught the opposite wall halfway down, and it shook with pants-dropping force every time the "L" went by; like that army fellow with the pompadour and gyrating hips I passed on for the lead in my last picture, *Exotic Woman and G.I. Sing*. Again, it was the hair that was my undoing. Instead, I went with Paul Lynde and paired him with a donkey wearing makeup. In my defense, talking animals were big at the time and the cost of peanut butter was lower than ever.

But I guess I let overzealousness get the better of me. Unfortunately, it wouldn't be the last time. The film was met with an outpouring of critical condemnation and prompted a number of amendments throughout both the film and cosmetics industries. So, when the phone rang, you bet I picked up. The pitch was vague, but at the time, I would have taken anything. An opportunity was an opportunity. And a dollar was a dollar. And my work was still my life, even if it was classified. I saw my comeback, shimmering with gold and illuminated in the brilliant lights of a corner marquee. Not on the west coast, but smackdab in the center of the country's capital, Washington D.C. A credit that, sadly, nobody would see. That is unless they had Level 7 clearance. But a marquee featuring a production so important it would stretch beyond Hollywood and the sleepy downtown theater of Anywhere, U.S.A., and instead be fed directly into every television set on the planet.

In the summer of 1966, we began principal photography on *Exodus: Earth*. That was our working title at the time—or codename, as the higher-ups liked to call it. But really, I'm getting ahead of myself. Let's go back for a moment, shall we? Let the screen dissolve with haunting waves and allow the music to transport us back in time.

The 1930s were a gas. Hollywood was glamorous and musicals reigned supreme. I was the hottest choreographer the studio had at its disposal, which was saying a lot given the fact I was their only musical director under contract not working exclusively with nude dancers. In 1933, I choreographed *Uniform Dames*, which was an absolute smash. My first hit. I was with Laminate Pictures and had been given free rein with all my numbers. And I never looked back. The following year I directed the musical sequences for three top-grossing pictures: *Spinning Pianos*, *Champagne Nights*, and that Stanley Bachwell showgirl classic, *The Weigh-In*, my first Academy Award contender. Which I lost to the film *Wartime Dreamscapes* and that dick, Richard

Smiteley. He empowered the girls by giving them rifles and poignant dialogue. I didn't know that was allowed. But I bounced back later that same year with the sensational number "A Chickadee's Two Cents" in Leonard Rouch's instant hit, *Glitzy Pants and a Matching Jacket*. At the time, we were unaware, but costume designer Margaret Miller-Shuster had designed the first-ever pantsuit. And although it wasn't the most appealing thing, it served its purpose.

Then one day, I got a phone call from the head of Laminate Pictures, Xavier J.B. Farrington, whom we all called Sal. It made perfect sense. He was a big cheese in Hollywood. But he was soft and an export, a foreigner, which made him stinky and easy to manipulate. So, I opened a box of soda biscuits and heard what he had to say.

"Reuben, my boy, I want you to make me a picture."

"Sure thing, Sal, I'd love to, but who's directing?"

"Why, you, of course. And Artie Mays."

"Co-direct, ya say?" I asked with period gusto. "Nah, I think I'm gonna skip that step in my career; try again."

"Reuben, my boy," he took another stab at it. "Direct me a picture yourself," he said. "And plaster your name, and only your name, over every inch of it."

"Sal, I'm over the moon—I'm speechless," I said while simultaneously writing down my fee in a ten-year contract with final cut and total take of ticket sales before sliding it across his desk. Also, we were in his office now.

There was no way this could come back on me. In those days, karma was a kind of donut. It was coated with sugar, and it was delicious. So naturally, being the cowardice, impotent pushover Sal was—and when I say that I say it with great affection—he accepted my offer. But not before I gave him a few notes on his performance, which included a cigar hanging from his mouth and the suggestion of leaning back in his chair to punctuate the offer with a robust and commanding tweed-stretched FUPA.

And so, we ran through the scene several more times until he got it right. And by "until he got it right," I mean we were losing light, and the crew was beginning to notice my tremors from withdrawal. Plus, I was already thinking of my next project.

Two months later, *Native Saul* hit theaters nationwide. My directorial debut. *Native Saul* was the completely original story of an outsider crawling up the Hollywood ladder, only to find he's afraid of heights and vastly unqualified. Lindsey Murdoch played wide-eyed studio bigwig Saul Rosenburgstein and delighted audiences with his heavenly falsetto. My dreams were taking off in an unimaginable direction, and the sky was the limit. Oh, how naive and more wrong I could not have been.

For twenty years, I made the biggest musicals with the biggest stars using the widest aspect ratios. My Kaleidocinemascope revolutionized the industry and bankrupted movie houses all across the country. Each seat in the theater came with a vomit bag, and we stole the prototype from Kenway Airlines, corner-to-corner. It was a career of immediate growth followed by a healthy and natural decline into failed television pilots. And I did it better than anyone. At the start of the 1940s, I had already directed two Oscar-nominated pictures: 1939's *Munchkin Parade* and the 1940 musical comedy *Barefoot Broadway Lady*, which followed small-town singer and dancer Dottie Ruth on her climb to the top or something. At that point in my career, I was very preoccupied with my outward appearance and lived day-in-and-day-out as more of a Hollywood trendsetter. I phoned in most of my adjustments for the actors, and I blocked all my scenes via telegram. I became so regularly absent from shooting that I asked the crew not to ruin the picture for me by giving away its plot. I epitomized celebrity wealth. I was so freakin' highlife, when I opened my mouth, people got a face full of Dom Perignon—and an ice-cold washcloth. I single-handedly killed the midnight blue tuxedo when I saw Mervyn Fleming in one at the premiere of Seymour Willie's animated marvel *Dancing Animals on LSD* and asked him if the insulation matched the wallpaper. It was too snappy a zing to question its logic. Men started carrying handkerchiefs in their breast pockets after they witnessed me at Lola Rogers's New Year's Eve bash wiping down the martini glass of my ex-wife, who died suddenly that night under mysterious circumstances.

The 1950s were a blur, fueled by unbridled ambition and a zircon habit I couldn't shake. I knew early on that trends were cyclical and that buying cheap ironically was cool. I got into some weird literature and started hanging out with people much poorer than myself. I was in search of new ideas. The drugs helped out with that almost immediately. The idea to dub Thelma Reed's desperate solo in *Lonely Backwoodsman* using the voices of three different actresses came to me while tripping berries and singing impromptu showtunes in my tri-mirrored vanity. I was firing on all creative cylinders. Sure, I may have made a few missteps along the way, but each of them was in the name of cinematic progress and narrative exploration.

In 1958, I did *It's a Topsy-Turvy World* with Bing Bixby. I shot the entire film with the camera upside down and made the cast walk on their hands. I knew I was on to something before I even had an inkling of what it was. And I rode that ambiguity all the way to release. I had possibly delivered the most insightful social commentary ever conveyed in a musical. But the critics hated it. They crucified me. They referred to my shows as mere stunts and called my routines "routine." Their criticism was solid B-level wit, and I couldn't knock 'em for that. Writer Spike Jenkins labeled me "dangerous" and put out an ad in Variety calling for a full-scale manhunt.

Heading into the 1960s, I moved from what I was calling experimental musical features to the vibrantly surreal subgenre of beach party films, which were making their way onto the scene. There was *Midriff Beach*, *Bikini Patrol*, and my personal favorite, *Goodbye Bush, Hello Go-Go*. But I was so out-of-touch with the youth. Plus, I couldn't keep up with their nonsensical, tongue-twisting, onomatopoeia-sounding lyrics. It was all just so unnecessary. Also, my susceptibility to swimmer's ear was out of control. Rain was a constant fear. The studio was struggling, and my short stint on the small screen didn't help. I shot the pilot for *Blackout* without removing the lens cap, so the audience at home could feel the blackout.

Shortly after, Laminate tanked, and the bank foreclosed on my Hollywood spread up in the hills, which had naturally taken on an open-door policy and was packed to the rafters with Bohemians, freethinkers, and a surprisingly reasonable water bill. In fact, the whole place was starting to give off a real L. Ron Hubbard vibe, if ya know what I mean. So, with nothing more than a padded bindle from the old Laminate props department, I bade farewell to the town that gave me everything and caught the 2:15 cattle train to Chicago.

I found work on the killing floor of the Schwager's Slaughterhouse courtesy of my fine traveling companions, who aided in making my first day on the job both fun and very uncomfortable. The pay was meager, and security was tight. We were a crafty crew, but the friskers were thorough. The spoils and opulence of my yesteryear were paraded in front of me as if a haunting reminder of my untamed hubris. I moved into a closet of a room on the West Side and spent my evenings dreaming of cocktail parties, swimming pools, and a bathroom on the same floor.

Then, on one distinctively ordinary evening, after drinking my fill of the neighbor's wine, the phone rang. And with noticeably more urgency, I might add—which is difficult to spot with a phone. You gotta listen closely, but it's there. I lifted the receiver and found my key light.

"Hello?"

"Mr., uh, Merriweather?"

It was the Commander-in-Chief himself, John Fitzgerald Kennedy. The accent was undeniable. It was the vocal equivalent of a twenty-four-dollar seafood platter with a Maryland crab cake and lite butter sauce. In the moment, I seized an opportunity.

"Happy Birthday, Mr. President," I said with my best impression of a barbiturate-filled marriage between sexy and sad. The president continued.

"Today, your country calls you up for service."

"What kind of service?" I asked, choking on my own pathetic dejection.

"I won't sugar coat it, 'Weather, we're in a tight spot. And I've got a pledge out there I best make good on come New Year's 1970."

You could hear it in his voice, and it was not the fresh catch of the day I was hoping for. Cue music.

In the early 60s, the country was in the middle of a space race, which was jump-started by two guys in big coats named Sputs and Nick, along with their Russian friend Yuri something. In response, the president promised to put a man on the moon by decade's end. The country was striving for global eminence. And at the time, I was spending Wednesday nights worshiping with a witchy cult by the reservoir. Apparently, things down south weren't progressing as quickly as Washington would have liked, and with things heating up in Vietnam, they were beginning to roll out the lifeboats.

"You want me to shoot a picture for the government?" I asked organically to move along the story.

"In a manner of speaking," Kennedy said. "We'll talk more later; I gotta split. I got this thing in Dallas."

And that was the last time we ever spoke...on the phone. Because the next time was in person six days later poolside at the Hollywood Palms in Los Angeles. That's right, baby! I was back. And with a red-carpet welcome, reveling in the plushy affluence of Hollywood's most decadent and discrete hotel for the glitterati elite—which included a visual buffet of flesh that required two beach towels to conceal my excitement. And as I stepped to the edge of the pool, I found myself staring at a ghost...John F. Koudini...risen from the grave, free of shackles, and diving head-first into a pair of 60s breasts. I was dumbfounded.

See, when the public started asking the question "Who killed Kennedy?" they should have been asking the more practical question: Was Kennedy really dead? Short answer with a question: Whadda you think? Shorter answer: No. Light in the loafers producer Shep Francis heard from his boy toy Texas governor that when Kennedy's car took the left on Elm Street, Jack turned to Jackie and said, "It's been real." Leave it to the politicians to have the forethought to ignite and feed the perpetuation of a conspiracy as a means of distraction. Ha! It was a number they could perform in their sleep, forwards and backwards—which is a weird way to dream. It's like that beautiful piece of advice screenwriter Melvin Sagoff gave me after my reverse-Mermaid musical *Fish Breath* flopped - "Write what you know."

And so there we were, drinking daiquiris, our bodies dripping with bronzer and roasting to cosmetic perfection under a gorgeous California sun in a cancer-less culture. Ha, the sun...how ironic.

"Mr. Merriweather?" The president turned to me, the light catching his ventriloquist dummy-like face, before uttering eight words that would affect the rest of my life in a profound and lasting way. He said..."I want you to fake the moon landing."

I was flabbergasted. So much to the degree, I didn't realize I was gettin' worked on under my towel by, as best I could tell, a silhouetted hive of hair.

"The moon landing?" I asked with boyish exuberance as a seventy-year-old man.

"Frankly, 'Weather," he tried to make it stick, "we don't have a clue of what we're doing, and it appears a few more years won't make an iota of difference. That's where you come in."

"Why me?" I asked, tickling at the heart of the story.

"We phoned all the top directors," he said. "Osborn, Samuels, Donen..." The president flattered to the delight of my ego. "...And none of them picked up."

Under my towel, the wet noodle express pulled into the station right on time.

"I see," I said, favoring the shady side of my deckchair. My answer was one of the painful kind, and suddenly, I felt cheap. But then, something awoke in me. I had been given a second chance—an opportunity to pull myself up out of the gutter and reclaim my legacy. And it filled my body with a confidence I hadn't felt since Mamie

Daltrey said I was the best she ever had…moments before I cast her as the female lead in *Adults Playing Teens*.

We were going to fake the moon landing. And from there, who knew…Venus, Neptune, Saturn?! I was looking at a multi-picture deal. It was a high no drug could match. Although that night we partied so A-list, the president fell off his balcony into a palm tree during a sex pyramid with actress Jodie Ray, the ensemble cast of 1961's Shakespearean gang musical *Foes in Love*, and the hotel's portly house detective, Buggs.

The next morning, we nursed our hangovers with eggs and top sirloin steak at The Griddle Stand and got to work.

From day one, the Space Program fostered the idea of a Plan-B in the event they couldn't meet their deadline. It was a tall order. And with a mass monkey grave nestled somewhere in the sunshine state, Washington was beginning to have their doubts. Enter a seemingly over-the-hill cinematic legend and a motorboating dead guy in the wake of a country in mourning. But where to execute such an elaborate scheme? D.C., Houston, Area 51? Which I had just learned was a thing. And then it hit me, like 3 AM indigestion…Hollywood. Where nothing is as it seems.

"We shoot the entire thing right under everybody's noses," I pitched the president, who was having a lot of trouble lowering the restaurant's blinds. "And we conceal every bit of it within the shooting schedule of a doomed film production." It was genius. But most importantly, general enough to evade any narrative copyrights that might appear in my memoir. First thing was first, though...we would need the perfect shell project. And I had just the film. *Goop from Space* was a two-hundred-page Sci-fi monster flick I wrote in one sitting several years earlier after doing heroin while wearing satin pajamas. It told the story of this multiplying glob from outer space that lands in a Midwest-looking town and starts eating its way up the food chain—derelicts, then neighborhood pets, and so on in that fashion. In the end, we find out that the goop is, in fact, space junk from a planet called Earth. That was the big Rod Serling one-two that nobody would see comin'. It was the perfect cover.

We purchased the dilapidated lots of Laminate Pictures, where we found my old punching bag Xavier J.B. Farrington—Sal from Act I— living in the rickety upstairs brothel from the *Peaceful Sheriff* set. We hosed him off at the studio stable, walloped him with oversized powder puffs, and reinstated him as chief executive of Laminate Pictures. Then we stuffed that studio fat like a Christmas goose, courtesy of taxpayer dollars funneled in through freaky government back channels. We fed the press a phony story about Farrington rebuilding his empire after turning a nickel from the storm drain into a fortune. It was a supporting rags-to-riches-to-rags-back-to-riches biopic that could only be the product of Hollywood—life's go-to for endless retakes.

Kennedy had split for Cuba with a chorus line of vivacious creatures and said he'd send me a postcard. But there would be no waiting by the mailbox...I had a picture to make. Before jetting, the K-man put me in touch with one of their own, a babysitter from

NASA. They called him the Rocketman. And since the only rocketmen I knew were in West Hollywood, I figured it was an alias. Rockets was to serve as the show's consultant and my Texas contact. Secrecy was paramount, and the truth of our labors, both east and west, had to remain independent of each other—they didn't know about us, and we didn't know about them. When people on the street would mention the Apollo missions during idle chit-chat, I'd rear back and shoot them this look like they didn't know what they were talking about. And it was Rockets's role to provide us with the material we needed to duplicate an authentic landing—specs, source photos, even the layouts for a possible product placement deal with Tang.

But Laminate had to look on the up and up. And with just a single picture in development, we were beginning to appear as the perfect underdog story, and that meant reporters and journalists we weren't paying. The studio had to produce. But nothing to critical acclaim. Just tight, middle-of-the-road mediocrity to keep us under the radar. Popcorn pushers. It was imperative that we stay one step alongside industry trends. So, I padded the studio with a production slate nobody would question.

He Represents the Voiceless was based on the courtroom novel of the same name, which we hired someone to write, then released through a sham publisher. A slapstick comedy about a nitwit minding a swanky hotel for his ill uncle called *Rung Bell*, with bits involving a lot of doors opening and closing. Looking for romance? Try *The Millionaire and the Nobody*, our period musical that promised expensive gowns, penthouse views, and a two-and-half-minute trailer that answered all the audience's questions. *The Endless Hour* was a G-rated war pic starring that famous Hollywood roughneck Howard Pyle, who we made up and went so far as to purchase a Beverly Hills house for, where we auditioned and cast a mother and two-point-five children to live. And let's not forget Laminate's little tech-heavy Sci-fi project shooting on Stage 7, *Goop from Space*, scheduled for release whenever Houston gave the signal. And directed by, what our own Hedda Hopper—Rita Hooper—wrote in a film journal we bankrolled, "That once celebrated musical master Ruben Merriweather in the desperate, eleventh hour of an apparent comeback." I took grievance but shelved it for my country. That night, though, I turned heads by going casual to a formal affair. It was just the fix I needed.

It was time to assemble a crew. Swish-pan!

To produce, I brought in the brightest and most illustrious from Hollywood's Golden Age of musicals, that iconic lyricist and production guru, Sid Sherman. Sid had sadly fallen out of the public eye in the 1950s after finding himself in a PR pickle spearheaded by the studio for not disclosing his affair with twelve-year-old actress Launa Tate to HR. If there was one thing Hollywood despised more than gossip, it was a disregard for office policy.

For the photography, I enlisted my main man, Reinhold Baker, who had filmed in Laos during the rebellions in 1960. He was there shooting a travel documentary on exotic foods. "Remember, legs mean protein!" Nobody could capture foreign landscapes better than Baker.

But behind the camera, I would need an eye for the surreal, someone who could take the audience to the moon emotionally. Manuel Santiago was the guy. A classically trained surrealist, Santiago was the most avant-garde they came. With a forty-year career featuring film history classics from that 1926 silent masterpiece *Ants on Food* to the 1961 treasure *Decomposing Animals*, I knew the moon's potential horrors would be conveyed honestly…and with gross irrational irony.

We were flirting with the point of no return and making all the right moves. The studio had a lineup you couldn't bribe someone to cover, and the hoax was receiving from us the perfect amount of attention. So we thought. But even after all those years, I still lacked wisdom. I was falling back into old habits. Blinded by superficialities and plagued by personal pitfalls. It was obvious I was losing perspective. We would have to go bigger. Much bigger. And further. Further than any production had gone before. Reach out into those vast stretches of the cinematic unknown and grab history by the balls and say we did. There was no equivalent to our endeavor. In the contrails of the nation's pursuit of glory, we would take movie magic to new heights, and it would be the longest and most trying production of my entire life.

(INTERMISSION)

Now, let's see, where were we?

Oh yeah…I was tasked with taking the world to the moon through the magic of movies. The United States had plunged itself headlong into an international pissing match, and the Cold War was heating up. Now, with a military blooper smack dab in the heart of Asia's rice bowl, the country would need a distraction bigger than Andy Taylor in color. A voyage through space was just the ticket.

In the summer of 1966, my studio put-on, Laminate Pictures, built as a front for faking the moon landing, was flourishing as Hollywood's best-kept secret. Our production *Goop from Space* was in full-on production mode, and the soundstage was bustling with a flurry of deception. It was exhilarating.

The art department had delivered us a moon worthy of the real thing. The surface was made of King's Kitty Litter trucked in for a family film we did fake posters for—then, to cover our tracks, wrote and produced for just under a mil. *Mr. Biscuit's Big Day* starred a one Freddie Douglas and that Russian Blue sensation Binkzy, the It-Cat of 1966—who we lured from the alley behind the studio. The moon rocks came from that city by the bay in the backroom of a little psychedelic shop at the corner of Haight and Ashbury, and work came to a screeching lull. The ideas were plentiful, but nobody wrote them down. Crater fragments were shipped in from our new "Aloha" neighbors to the west, Hawaii, which remains the only place on the planet you can get chocolate with macadamias. We had four versions of the lunar module: one replica to-scale for exteriors, two half modules, and one painted black and white that we would shoot in color. We spared no expense. In fact, we were the only studio in town providing our production assistants with furnished offices and annual allowances for cosmetic work. The guys in the mailroom got new Cadillacs and designer hairpieces for those that fell victim to God calling it a day at 4:45. The secretaries were paid by the word, and our riggers were fashioned with the finest flannels from Europe. And it was all paid for by the American people. Progress comes at a price, or they don't come at all.

I purchased the haunted home of silent film swashbuckler Max Kaplan in Whitley Heights and used the guest house as my office. With a measly five bedrooms, fireplace, and pool with grotto, it was tight, but quaint and free of distraction. At night, I toiled away, revising pages while blaring free-form jazz for focus and clarity. The words flowed from me with harmonious sustain, like the Kamikaze precision of Lenny Tate rolling over the snares, or the chaotic wail of Rex Redding's heavenly sax. And that was just the screen direction. Within nine short months, I had conceived the perfect smokescreen for our *Goop from Space* cover. It was half a page and depicted a ship of celestial sanitation workers from Earth with ties to the galactic teamsters, dumping the title goop into space. It was masterful.

NASA had chosen their flight crew and sent over the headshots. They were calling the mission Apollo 1, which was a shout-out to soul greats like James Brown and Patti LaBelle. We all thought it was pretty cool. To play the astronauts—aka Space Garbage Man #1 and Space Garbage Man #2, plus Space Garbage Man #3, who would be in the scene and credited but not remembered—I phoned up my old standbys Frank Pear and James Eldridge from *Barefoot*. They had just the right about of dashing to play American astronauts. They had two-buck haircuts and were tan. And that was pretty much it. But it was thirty-five years later, and they were living up their twilight years being pampered in the lavish confines of the Beverly Springs Rest Home. So, I staked out Grauman's to find their forty-year-old doubles for what I had envisioned as some sort of *Merrily We Roll Along* shtick. Only successful. What can I say? I was loyal. Some would say to a fault. At the end of the day, I had signed an accountant from Arkansas and a bank teller with the same size feet as Vera Miles. Then I cut my friends a check for their time and gave them both an associate producer credit on the "film."

But, to play the moon landing's heroic command pilot, I would need a personality that was out of this world. So, I booked a first-class ticket to the closest place a sunny west coast native would look for otherworldly beings and went searching for a star...New York City.

I knew the first man on the moon had to have a sizzle only Broadway could provide. George Caldwell had the hottest name on the block. We would have to use his birth name, which had a lot more syllables. He was performing in two shows: *Matchmaker in Love* and *Racy Dinner Theater*, which was a show about abortion. Caldwell was brilliant. I laughed. I cried. I was even a little turned on. We got to know each other real well inside what I thought was a camera obscura in a smutty theater on 42nd at Seventh Avenue—then never wanted to see each other again. So, I returned to Hollywood with his twin brother, Beauford, who had no acting experience whatsoever. But it didn't matter. He looked the part, and I could look him in the eyes without throwing up a little. We had our cast.

Then one day, I got a call on the stage phone, the red one. I rolled my eyes and began channeling strength. It was the Rocketman, our government gofer and a pain in my ass.

"Ruben, it's Rockets."

"Weird, I thought it was Dorothy Sims inviting me into her dressing room."

"We've been talking things over, and we're not thrilled about the title."

"What, *Goop from Space?*"

"We were thinkin' *Exodus: Earth.*"

Apparently, Houston had been kicking their heels waiting out the clock or something and thought they were movie producers. Like a cat on cashmere, I lost it. I fired the next person I saw and kicked them to the curb with keys to a slightly used Oldsmobile and a check for a deposit on a bodega. The economy was ripe for a small business, but they would have to put in the effort—I was livid.

"Oh, and another thing..." Rockets was just warming up. "It's about the photo."

In trying to keep our plot contained, I sealed up all the stage exits each day and manned them with armed guards in riot gear. Interesting fact: Those guards would go on to serve for the Ohio National Guard.

And with yet another device designed to help us appear above-board, we ran daily studio tours with big trams and androgynous guides with perfect teeth. Twenty tours a day, seven days a week. Apparently, some Carolina rube snapped a photo of one of the guards, and that barren, big mouth Mamie Dickers wrote it up in her column. Washington freaked out.

"Some of the higher-ups see it as unwanted attention," Rockets said before pausing for a sip of what sounded like Tab. "Hollywood's a sewing circle; we want to move the operation to Burbank."

I saw red, then immediately locked eyes with a paid intern and readied my checkbook like a big-time Hollywood gunslinger. Burbank? Were they joking?

"It's a matter of confidentiality," Rockets said. "Which is this new umbrella term we've adopted for when people ask us reasonable questions."

The United States government was about to clean house and really start cashing in on this whole capitalism thing. And we're talking mucho dinero, so money was no object. But they would need help—their first recruit: Hollywood. Initially with me, then with that Bonzo lover, Ronald "Saddle Sore" Reagan. The two would get along nicely. Reagan was a yes man, but I fought back. I'll be goddamned if I was going to commute over the hill.

"Now you listen here, and you listen good, you pocket protector with a pulse." My boosters ignited. "It's like thirty minutes each way," I screamed into the phone in front of the crew. "And that's on a good day!" I went for the jugular. "Plus, you can't get a decent steak in the

Valley. And if you think for one flippin' second, I'm going to reduce myself to a charcoal ribeye with ketchup, like some Rabbi with an inefficiency for grilling, you got another thing comin', Jack!"

Like anyone of once great wealth and prestige, I expected a similar quality of excellence now in my second circle. If I had learned one thing during my time in the pits, it's that it sucked, and I would avoid it like how all of Hollywood in the 1950s avoided actor Donovan Bloomberg's all-red Fourth of July party. Rockets continued.

"We're hearing skepticism among the public, and we want to nip that chatter in the bud."

"That's great, Rockets, but what's that got to do with me?"

"We want to do the show live."

Live? The word echoed with weight. I dropped the phone and steadied myself, trembling at the thought. There was no notion more terrifying to an obsessive director. Suddenly, my vision went soft, and my body fell limp. I collapsed to the studio floor, and my light faded to darkness.

I had been diagnosed with a migraine and ordered to stay in bed for a week. I got the rest I needed, but mainly just wore a robe for seven days. After feeling able, I sat in the window with a pontificating pose. Shoot the fake-moon-landing live? Were they insane? We were projecting to deceive an audience of four hundred million that day. The fact of the matter was crippling. I was going to need time.

So, I took a month off and got my head straight. I sat by overcast pools in discreet sweaters and read clothbound books in unorthodox places. I closeted my dancing shoes and cut parties cold turkey.

Then I called up an old buddy of mine, Gordon Geer, who was a big deal in radio back in the day—famously for his Saturday night WOK broadcast recorded live from the Peking Karaoke Cafe in Chinatown, as well as his directorial work on *Brunch with Bruce and Ethyl*, which was a talk radio program about car maintenance. I was seeking words of wisdom. He said, "Mickey..." Gordon had been out to lunch for years and forgot to leave a warm body at reception, if you know what I mean.

"Mickey...speak from the heart," he said. "Be true to yourself. And remember to blanch the Brussels sprouts before seasoning them."

He was right. I could never get them to restaurant tenderness. But more importantly, I had been ignoring my impulses. It was my shoot-from-the-hip essence that had taken me to the top in the first place. My thirst for innovation, which I quenched by any means necessary. Who had I become? A puppet doing the government's bidding. I had lost my loose values...my edge...my voice. Right then and there, I accepted the challenge of shooting live, but vowed to do it my way. I was going to propel mankind into the 21st century the Rueben Merriweather way—with style, extravagance, and a complete disregard for the material.

Two months later—thanks to government bribes and a bundle of six weeks all-expense-paid trips to Mexico that were given out to the city's entire building division department, including permit officials and inspectors—Laminate Pictures cut the ribbon on its new Burbank studio. It was a sheer marvel. I was proud to call it my idea. There were thirty sound stages, each of twenty thousand plus square feet, million-gallon water tanks, and a seven-story tall perimeter wall you could see from space; until we scrubbed it from the satellite feed. The stages were equipped with state-of-the-art control rooms for live recordings and broadcasts, in addition to high-capacity stadium seating; in the event, one day, everything leaked out and American audiences took to this kind of deception as a form of entertainment. Stage 24, the studio's jewel, was constructed with an unprecedented sixty-foot-high dome rising into the sky, perfect for Laminate's now large-scale retooled Sci-fi project we were calling *Exodus: Earth*. And when I say "we," I'm speaking on behalf of the slate and several scripts that were holding open a door. And even those, *Exodus: Earth* was in quotes. Inside, the lunar surface had never looked so grand. Watching the command module being lowered for the first time from the observatory onto what we were calling Moon 2.0—which none of us understood—was an experience that could only be described as unrestrained awe. It was magnificent and truly out of sight. Also, I had had a cup of mushroom tea with my morning marmalade and was tripping pretty good.

At that moment, my feet left the stage. Floating and spinning through space in a perfectly placed Act II-Act III transitional dream sequence, I swirled about the stars with the wave of my hand, then plucked the moon from the cosmos and swallowed it. My body liquefied, and my face morphed. Our bodies merged into one—my eyes, blinking craters. I continued falling before coming to rest upon a starless plane. Lifeless, time accelerated. My body was born from the soil, and copies followed. Villages went up. Towns, cities. We united with a distant civilization, then joined hands and sang something public domain. We broke bread, we loved, we fought, we divided. Then there was nothingness. I was alone in space, screaming in silence, and surrounded by infinite emptiness. Oh, shit, it was a bad trip! My body filled with doubt. I panicked and focused only on my panicking intensifying. I gasped for air and found myself strapped to a reclined chair in a theater in my brain, watching images projected onto the inside wall of my skull—homes decimated by blasts of orange tint, vacant playground equipment turned to dust. Annihilation. Uncle Sam being blown by an obscure figure wearing my favorite trousers. Birth. Death. Repeat. I screamed with horror as my audio dropped in and out of sync, and I returned to Earth. And my feet, back to the stage.

The hallucinations subsided, and I found myself wrapped up in the set's colossal backdrop curtain. The universe was speaking to me. And every word was coming in loud and clear. I was on the right track.

Rehearsals were coming along beautifully, and as much as I hated to admit it, the extra time in the car each morning was nice. I knew every song on the radio. But on January 27, 1967, tragedy struck when all three Apollo 1 astronauts were killed during a launch rehearsal. It was a devastating blow. We would have to recast. I had too much artistic integrity to jeopardize the authenticity of the conspiracy. Firing Beauford and those other two was the hardest thing I've ever had to do. Was it a setback? You bet. But nothing that couldn't be cured with a lively montage showcasing the passage of time. Hit it!

The next two years would be a seemingly endless cycle of casting and recasting in the wake of NASA's efforts to preserve its dignity, like a middle-aged man being walked in on while taking a bath. After the Apollo 1 disaster, blasting onto the scene in natural succession were Apollo Missions 4 through 6. These were unmanned flights using NASA's new fancy-schmancy rocket—the fully loaded Saturn S-series. It was cobbled together with secondhand Russian parts sent for by mail order and bought on time. Soon everybody would have one. Like a starter rocket you could bang up a little.

October 1968 saw Apollo 7 and the return of the astronauts. For the first time in history, the country watched Americans in space, puttering around in low orbit. And NASA dangled that low-hanging fruit in front of audiences like a shiny object and got the ratings boost they were looking for. We responded by putting out a casting call for a hundred little people to play sunflowers in some flying car musical, then dressed them up as funny moon people. It was on. NASA started getting closer to the moon, so we filled it with dancing girls. They reached the moon's orbit; we started rumors about their sons wearing dresses. The sands were racing through the hourglass as America watched on with bated breath, hoping glory would come calling.

1969...I was seventy-six years old, and everything was different. Hippies drove around in Nazi cars, and the Beatles concluded their extraordinary five-year-long trial of a promising hair growth pharmaceutical. It was a cultural awakening.

The production was bigger and more colorful than ever. Our small yet ever-changing cast of cosmic flyboys had grown into an ensemble and was supported by two hundred extras and a chorus line of curvy, green-stemmed Martians. They were sure to drive Earthmen wild. Plus, they had that out-of-town allure.

But we didn't just want something that was showy. Times were changing, and we were changing with them. This was an era ruled by social renegades. So, we hitched a ride on the bandwagon and entered the march. There was never a more qualified group. But we would need a message that could counter our moon's grandiose and tempting facade. Civil Rights, Vietnam, the labor movement—these would not be addressed. So, instead, we gave audiences what they wanted, the issues that would have them clamoring for years. And at the top of the list—serial murderers. They were captivating and sexualized, which was a little weird. In the summer of '69, the Zodiac killer was getting his rocks off by slaying couples in California, and the public ate it up with a spoon. The Zodiac was even taking credit for stuff he didn't even do, like people dying in their sleep or having a heart attack trying to put on summer shorts. And it didn't get more American than that. The moon needed a killer to convey our country's loss of innocence or something.

Also, the fast-food industry was skyrocketing, so we conceived the lunar restaurant chain Moon Burger, which was a treat for moon families after moon worship, even though their moon children weren't behaving and didn't deserve it.

Additionally, the pill was outlawed by the Pope, and its safety was called into question by leading manufacturers of condoms. Women were up in arms. But not as much as men. The moon would have to be a skin-to-skin hedonistic haven, representing free love with zero repercussions. These three things would serve as the core of our moon landing commentary.

My director of photography, Reinhold Baker, and his extreme-leftist cameraman, Manuel Santiago, also embraced the revolution by wearing berets and buttons. They had the 1ˢᵗ rub dirt into the lens to convey the raw and gritty nature of the people's uprising. It would play beautifully against the lavish musical number I wrote and choreographed for the moon's inhabitants upon the astronauts' arrival, which included thirty-four planned sweeping cane shots and five costume changes.

And in the roles of the visiting Apollo 11 earthlings—who were publicly announced on January 7, 1969, to be Neil Armstrong and Buzz "Iron Fists" Aldrin—I was lucky enough to snag the two rising stars from the acclaimed 1966 experimental underground film *Motel Drag*, by influential visual artist and outed grape tickler, Teddy Toots. Their names were Poppins and Neon, and they were members of Toots's pool of young, rough-faced amateur actors known as Teddy's Tots. Poppins and Neon both came from wealthy New York families, so we could save money on an elaborate alibi since nobody would come looking for them. Everything was set. Our moon was honest, intelligent, and goddamn spectacular. It was the moon America deserved.

But I couldn't help thinking things had gotten a bit muddled. Had I let the project get away from me? I knew at the time I was talking crazy, but still, I couldn't let the crew overhear my soliloquy. I wasn't a man known for questioning himself or even acknowledging outside opinions. Nevertheless, I felt a compulsion. I needed to talk to someone.

So, I donned an ensemble of white, baggy linen and caught the first single-engine death trap to the harsh tropical wildernesses of the Caribbean to look up an old friend. I scoured the colorful shantytown of Trinidad de Cuba and sought help from the locals.

"Señor Presidente?" I asked one of the first ten men I saw with a bicycle and a chicken. "Señor Presidente?" I pleaded with a raggedy street band in mid-chorus. The sadness of their condition revealed itself with one powerful cliché after another. The jungle was unforgiving, and its people were so destitute they ate only plantains and couldn't even speak English. My heart broke for them.

Suddenly, a boy of twenty-nine with shiny loafers and an unfiltered cigarillo, leaning against a brand new thirty-year-old convertible, got my attention and ushered me up the hill to a large colonial plantation house. I was heading deeper into the heart of the unpleasantness. I was greeted at the door by a sultry Cuban dish in red—a harlot in fine silks. She escorted me into a den with high-back chairs and oddly positioned electrical outlets. I didn't know what to make of it all. On the one hand, it was nice, but on the other hand, it was different, and this caused me vexation. Then, not a moment too soon, I found a familiar face.

"'Weather…it's so good to see you."

It was Kennedy, rocking a beard and hair down to his shoulders.

"Jack." We shared a much-needed embrace.

"Come…let's catch up," Kennedy said. "We'll sit in the *pahlah*."

And so there we were, drinking rum and smoking big fat cigars while reminiscing. But there were girls around, so it wasn't weird.

"So, 'Weather, what brings you down this way? Hey, how'd that moon thing go?" he asked, brushing the hair from his face with ambiguous sexuality.

"Actually, Jack, I could use some guidance."

"Need some oomph, huh? Here, try this old, isolated soda pop ingredient that's exploding down south," he said, tapping out a line of cocaine onto a four-hundred-year-old Louis de Bastall cocaine table.

It was a hundred miles per hour in the opposite direction.

"I was thinking more of a sit down with mission control," I said to be polite, not wanting to come across as too eager. "OK, maybe just a taste."

And I didn't sleep for five days. I built a cabana shirtless using only a saw, then met five of Kennedy's eight new families. It was the pick-up I was looking for.

Upon my return, I took the project up a notch and matched its energy with unkempt facial hair and loud Hawaiian shirts and I made sure to remain on edge for most of the day. After that, things got kooky, and rehearsals ran 'round the clock. I demanded perfection. We were on the cusp of brilliance and quite possibly an entirely new visual medium altogether, as our moon landing had taken the form of six different genres being executed simultaneously. Also, there would be multiple scenes of live sex and undiluted penetration. But we'd do it tastefully.

We were redefining space travel.

But it was all over. I had been at the helm of a ghost production, shrouded in fog and fueled by a craft services table of narcotics and a crew whose names I barely knew. And emerging from the fog—an iceberg as big as the moon. I'll never forget the day I walked onto that stage and saw the grainy black and white images of my future being played out by a glorified ape in a big white monkey suit. The set was at a standstill, and every pair of eyes were glued to a monitor. The static-filled voice of Neil Armstrong reverberated out to every corner of the stage. And my heart sank.

"That's one small step for man, one giant leap for mankind."

Motherfucker. It was good. It was real good. It was downright perfect. And I was about to be sick.

"Crewcuts" and "Punchy" had sucked all the air out of the room and left us with nothing but misery. No cheers. No champagne. No ticker-tape parade with a Midwest beauty queen. On the screen, they gloated and rubbed our faces in it. All their prancing around out there—we knew who it was meant for. The studio quietly dispersed like a deflated mayoral campaign, and I was in a state of disbelief.

Like the decades, the cast and crew washed over me with a solitary consoling pat on the back. And that was it. We were shut down. Kill the lights...Exchange phone numbers...Secure another job before leaving the set. We had created a multi-million-dollar movie studio with countless successful franchises and impressive quarterly earnings and had nothing to show for it. I had failed.

In the end, NASA faked the moon landing on their own on some soundstage out in the desert using a production company that primarily made PSA films about teenage delinquency. The Apollo Program would go on to make five sequels, each more ridiculous than the last. And they would do it by conning one hopeful production after another. If you're going to steal, steal from the best, am I right?

But by 1972, the moon was played, and the damage was already done. It was the beginning of the end for Hollywood. In the following years, the studio system would take back the reins and the money men would reclaim their thrones. Independent visionaries would be given the heave-ho and directions to the freeway—and they would not be direct. It was the death of cinematic artistry and the birth of risk management and film school loans.

As for me? What can I say? I had a good run. But, like Icarus, I flew too close to the sun on wings of celluloid, and it was time for me to exit frame. Sad thing of it is, I wouldn't even be shown the courtesy of a stage cross. Now, my life has been diminished to a sparse bungalow a mile off the PCH and a part-time position washing dishes for some chicken place with a casual attitude toward salmonella.

I am on my final reel. There are no more scores or chorus lines of pretty girls, no big premieres or Hollywood soirées, no grand farewell or meaningful revelation. The end for Ruben Merriweather is near. Fade to black. Roll credits.

Wait, I got it! A journey to the center of the earth! Huh? Wouldn't that be great? Bunch o' molten rock people dancing about. Is there a government agency for that? *Core: The Final, FINAL Frontier.* Ooh, or Bigfoot! No, lizard people! Yeah! Yeah, lizard people. *The Scales Walk Among Us...Cold-Blooded Killers...*You know they control the entire planet?

Romantics Anonymous

Hi, everyone. My name is Thaddeus, and I'm a romantic.

"Hi, Thaddeus."

I've been a romantic all my life, and I am powerless when it comes to controlling my romanticizing. Can we turn the music off? It's only enabling. The days of gay melodies resounding throughout my head, ushering in flights of fancy, are behind me. It's been a struggle, but I've been realistic for two years now. It's my cynicism that's kept me grounded. I no longer ponder seemingly trivial matters simply for the sake of enjoyment or self-expression. These days, my whimsical musings have been replaced with empty rhetoric and fantasy leagues. I mean, rotisserie leagues. Fantasy's a trigger word. As is rotisserie, but that's for an entirely different group. Now, through willpower and discipline, I use phrases like "cold approach" and "restraining order," as well as "401(k)," which sounds much more immediately lucrative than it is. But I digress. I've completely turned my life around thanks to Romantics Anonymous. It showed me the true path to salvation. No more purple prose for me—I'm clean. It's nothing but practical, uninspired assessments from here on out.

I'd be lying, though, if I stood up here and said it's gotten easier over time. I don't think it ever gets easier. It's still difficult not to lose myself in the beauty of a cloud formation or the smell of freshly cut grass in the summertime. The road to recovery's been a bumpy one, paved with fanciful tangents and imaginative impulses. But at the end of that road, rationality. And a clear head ready to absorb life's rewarding social biases and regurgitated ideas, free of emotion and fueled by personal gain. It's nice. Conformity is my new addiction.

I've come a long way. God, I used to— I used to find magic in the mundane and whimsy all around me. Ha, isn't that pathetic? I used to marvel at an autumn sunset and think life was grand. Thank God that's out of my system. I'm a regimented thinker now. No longer do things simply enter my brain willy-nilly without first being vetted or conveyed to me by someone else. It's a godsend. It really is. I don't have the strength or patience for original thought anymore. What a miserable disservice I put myself through for all those years. No more concepts embellished by my own destructive, long-winded tendencies. No more solitary moments stolen throughout the day to pontificate or ask why. And why would I when all the heavy lifting's already been done. I should clarify, that was, of course, a rhetorical question and in no way a philosophical inquiry. Ha, no uncertainty to see here. I'm on the straight and narrow.

Today, I stand here before you, my diction brief and to the point. The only thing flowery in my life is cultivated in a greenhouse. And not one of those up in the emerald triangle if you catch my drift. That stuff does more harm than good for someone in my condition. Expressive theorizing, free of calories and night sweats. Non-habit forming and eye-opening. Mind-altering. A companion with whom to stroll the city and bask in the sunlight. The warmth wrapping around my body like a— Sorry, sorry, sorry, sorry. Damn. See? No matter how strong you are or how well you think you've got things in check, it's still a daily battle. But it does get less frequent—the urges. Your cravings begin to weaken, and your capacity for conciseness and coldhearted indifference grows. I curb the compulsions by reserving my thoughts and beliefs for primetime cable and pushing the value of goods and services. Because, you know, when you boil it all down, that's where it's at. That's the good stuff in life. The true meaning of it all. The tangible. Stuff you can show off. Stuff that links you to a specific class. Believe me, no amount of nostalgia can match the high you get from being included. Am I right? I'm sure all of us here can attest to that. You gotta let that special spark that's within you fizzle out already. It's only holding you back, denying you of true progress and all the joys life has to offer. Toe the line already; your life depends on it. I don't mean to get preachy, it's just— it's just I'm so happy right now. Happy where I am. But most importantly, I'm happy with myself for the first time in a long time. I don't have to concern myself with being moved. I'm complacent, and it feels awesome.

Still, there's regret. That never goes away. And that's OK. You go through your steps. You learn to live with it. But it certainly doesn't take away from— Nothing will let me forget the fact that I hurt those closest to me, that I forced onto them unending runs of lyrical language and picturesque imagery. And optimism. So much fucking optimism. I once treated someone that had less than me as a person. How sad is that? I used to speak to people instead of their presumed social role. And I did it all so sincerely. I riffed without regard and took pleasure in the amusement and happiness of others. I didn't even care. Smiles, expression, growth—I took it all. I was out of control. My lips spewed passion into the ears of friends and family, even strangers, and forced them to think and feel. I cheated them out of seconds and, in worst cases, minutes that could have been better spent on social media and avoiding retail stores. I didn't realize how far gone I really was. When my friends found me, I was sitting in a window with a cup of tea, staring up at the stars contemplating existence and existentialism and having just a really nice time. I needed help.

Did you know my ideas used to be varied and my own? Ha, pitiful, I know. Just saying it fills me with such shame. God, what the fuck was I thinking? I guess I just— I guess I thought there was more to life than cultural fads and social constructs. I know it's silly. But what can I say? I was making my own decisions and wandered into the realm of independent thought.

I remember one day…I'll never forget it…I was out for a walk. It was the first day of fall and I needed a fix—daydreaming and free-associating—my reveries of choice at the time. The air was amazing. The season's first gust of wind kissing my cheek and projecting me to another time. An alternate childhood with leaves and a big porch that wrapped around the house. The impossible wasn't just plausible; it was a guarantee. A constant I willed from dreams and sensations— And oh, shit, shit, sorry! Sorry. Goddamnit. I don't mean to curse— It's just— Fuck— It's difficult. We need someone running a light in the back or something.

Even after years of progress, a realistic mindset or not, I will always be a romantic. And that's what you have to remember. Like many of you, I've made amends with those I caused joy, and they forgave me. Can I forgive myself? Can you forgive yourself? Tough to answer. It's part of the struggle. I play a lot of frisbee golf—that's been helping. I'm dating again. And I'm in love. I can't wait to meet her. I'm working out a lot and bettering myself where it counts. The glutes. But no gluten. I'm starting to use words like whey and BMI, and I'm dropping them into conversations that don't remotely call for them. It's just great to have this train back on the tracks. This disease...and it is a disease...will fill your life with color and expression like you've never known. And every second of it will pull you further and further away from reality. You'll be lost in a world without supply and demand. A world free of artistic monetization. It's a depressing thought, I know. And you can kiss living in excess goodbye. Hell, say a prayer for urbanization while you're at it. I don't mean to scare you, but it's the truth. Maybe some of you out there are living in that world right now. That's why I'm here to tell you it's not too late. You can decide to give in this very moment if you want. You owe it to yourself. Life— Life's short. Fall in line and get the most out of it. Because without collective identity...you're nothing. Thank— Thank you.

A Trip to Wine Country

*W*ith the California harvest in full swing, wine enthusiasts from across the country are staggering in droves to take in the North Coast's bubbly local color, as well as, and more importantly, to sample and shell out top dollar for bottle-after-bottle produced from the area's premier grapes. Whether it's a lively, interactive experience you're after—bouncing from earthy and awkward crush parties to a spirited hazing of the vine in a celebrated late-season ritual, each with woodfired pizzas and an attractive non-member attendance fee, or a more laid-back approach, taking in a sunset vista with a single gratis glass of a spicy Cabernet Franc and a wedge of moldy brie, calmly nursing a sunburn or frostbite while showing off elegant toe jewelry—this vast and world-famous appellation provides a plethora of tasty and shameless excursions. The kind made sadder with sun hats. And with notable wineries peppered throughout a wealth of distinct regions masterfully utilizing the area's cool, unrivaled climate and complex soil system, the selections on offer seem limitless. Beyond the top-label, award-winning cabernets and leading chardonnays churned out by the northern California giants, visitors looking for that perfect wine country destination will find a surprising host of lesser-known wineries and sub-appellations, each offering their own unique aesthetic and specialized brand of winemaking. From the application of traditional to modern techniques, the following is a list of five rising names in the world of North Coast wineries:

Rascalford Vineyards

Nestled in the moist and fertile valley of the Santa Martin wine region, Rascalford Vineyards is an innovator in the field of biodynamic winemaking and holistic farming. Winners of the 2012 Santa Martin Sustainable Winery of the Year presented by the Rhode Island International Wine and Spirits Competition, Rascalford employs an approach to viniculture advertised as "a harmonious wholeness to the process." Founded by Emilee Rascalford, a central figure in the development of the Santa Martin wine region in the early 1970s, as well as a great adorer of late-nineteenth-century European flair—rouge velvet and clawfoot furniture, which embellishes his vineyards and production areas—Rascalford characterizes their brand as "refined nature."

The eccentric and notably theatrical vintner's knowledge of the land dates back to the area's original winery established by Jules-Valentine Martin in 1874. Rascalford worked for Martin in the 1930s as the plant's senior mice extractor for nearly three decades. There, he was given a screened-ladle and a secondhand master's degree in organic cultivation and harvesting. He adopted and nurtured a love and reverence for Martin's legendary farming techniques and soil-to-glass process—a systematic approach that led Rascalford Vineyards to their award-winning 2010 Pink Petal Rosé. Which is portrayed as having "a dry, full-moon taste with ash and a hint of magic," fascinatingly produced from pinot noir grapes yielded in rich limestone, covered during the day, and cultivated at night by moisture and moonlight.

Emilee was a driven and outlandish young winemaker from the Martin School who ignited a modern love affair with an old tradition when he established his own winery in 1973. Maintaining his conviction that ripening grapes soak up every element of their environment, Rascalford installed loudspeakers across sixty acres of vineyards to serenade the grapes continually. Their 2015 Sauvignon Blanc Franz Wax-Abel Piano Concerto in D Minor was given a double-gold award at the highly coveted Catalina Wine Awards and Dolphin Show and is characterized as "a light and flowery gooseberry white with nimble notes of feathery octaves." Another double-gold recipient was their late-harvest holiday dessert wine—the 2016 Clove Port-Style Kozlovsky's March of the Gingerbread Men—presented at the annual Mt. Clair Wine Merchants Festival, which Rascalford calls "a festive red with plum and peppermint notes accented with a blend of silver and gold flakes complemented by chocolate, hearty fruit pies, or a mint and ginger-salt lick-stick during a gay winter stroll through the stark winter vineyards."

Additionally, in other highly rated varieties, Rascalford's viticulturists screen foreign films for the grapes on Friday nights during the summer. This process allows the romance, philosophies, and democratic innovation of the Old World to bleed into the grapes. The culture is conveyed through the skin and absorbed by the seeds, the soul of the fruit. Rascalford describes their 2016 Italian Neorealism Cabernet Sauvignon series as "a casual exchange expressed with passion, tobacco, and flights of post-war poverty." Rascalford Vineyards, in their myriad of revolutionary methods, also employs wine fornicators to stimulate the grapes. The presence of passionate and inspired lovemaking by two individuals of alternating genders, depending on the desired variety of the wine, provides the grapes with increased levels of scientifically measured sensuality. During the springtime bud break, visitors to Rascalford Vineyards are invited to attend the winery's highly anticipated consummation celebration—a formal, open-air gala featuring special guest fornicators from San Francisco's famous Shalowitz Brothers Theater, as well as a number of their distinguished plow mules.

Copperberry Estates

Those seeking a more atmospheric experience look no further than Copperberry Estates, set against the spectacular Red River Hills and neighboring the dry Mendocino Reservoir. Part of the thriving San

Lobos Valley wine region, connected by a network of wine trains with classy period dining cars and simulated privilege, Copperberry Estates offers visitors a tranquil, gastro-approach to tasting. The successful "Keep Their Mouths Full" philosophy developed by Copperberry CEO Cal Christie, a former amusement parks magnate and owner of the Pittsburgh Opossums (as well as a national pecan brand), places particular importance on spectacle, congested serenity, and sensory overload.

A large, Tuscany-inspired winery of tile and terracotta, with brightly colored frescos and indoor fountains, Copperberry Estates arrests its visitors' senses with lute players and an impressive afternoon cheese cart. Shops on either side of the Valletta Tasting Room allow visitors the opportunity to purchase Copperberry wine glasses and logo golf balls, as well as novelty T-shirts and refrigerator magnets with kitschy wine puns and self-help numbers. An open-air tram takes visitors on a ten-minute tour of the Copperberry vineyards from a sixty-mile-an-hour vantage point along the new Mayor Ana Ramirez Chardonnay Scenic Highway.

Recipients of the 2013 top honor Riesling at the esteemed Washington Lakes Wine Competition, Copperberry Estates specializes in sweet and sparkling white wines that are fruit-centered, with fresh levels of acidity, added sugar, and served with a shot of insulin. Their approach to winemaking is more relaxed and encompasses both old and new techniques—old in presentation and new in execution. Visitors will find vintage wood barrels littering the winery and its cellar, where they're given a guided audio tour while following a path of purple-painted grapes on the floor; even though Copperberry Estates processes and ages their white wines in modern-day stainless-steel tanks at an off-site plant, restricted to the public, as well as the TTB and FDA.

In 2017, after purchasing a large land plot north of the winery, owner Cal Christie announced plans for a massive one-hundred-acre Copperberry Estates theme park scheduled to open in 2024. The park will consist of sections including Pinot Grigio Point, Vinoland, and Chianti Corner, modeled after different regions in Italy, complete with accurate topography, five-star restaurants, and authentic racial stereotypes.

Jessup Farms

Ninety minutes outside Sacramento, the area of Marian Rock may not be the most widely known wine region in the North Coast or even the most populated, but those who manage to make their way up to the higher-elevated, more-inland sub-appellation will find the quaint getaway of Jessup Farms—providers of arguably the most faithful and attentive winery experience available in the country. A small, family-owned operation dedicated to wine education through a more hands-on approach, Jessup Farms places visitors right in the middle of the action by enrolling them in a multitude of fun and captivating activities, from picking and crushing to the lab and bottling.

Proud winners of the 2014 Shiraz Winery of the Year by the New York-based International Wine and Spirit Challenge—produced from a single varietal after the grape was introduced to the warmer, mountainous area in a partnership with Espresso Buds Winery outside Portland—the Jessup family opened their gates to the public in 1989. Built by the sweat of their brows, Zachariah Jessup and his wife Annabelle took a page from what they call "simpler times" when implementing the charmingly antiquated principles of their award-winning winery and inn. For the full experience, visitors are encouraged to begin with Jessup Farms' educational harvesting workshop. Here, guests will begin work at 2 AM, handpicking grapes one at a time. Giant spotlights allow visitors to see in the dark while at the same time illuminating any layabouts or deserters. For those that do wander off, an armed associate of Jessup Farms will escort them back to the fields.

Next, after the sun rises majestically over the Paluma Mountains, it's off to the stomp and destemming area. Guests are given a brief, energetic crash course in crushing grapes with their feet, usually presented in a foreign language and with heightened urgency, as time and production are of the essence in this crucial process. Guests not wanting to participate or found taking unapproved rests are asked to wait inside the rustically delightful Summer Room, a spaciously cozy metal closet situated in a field by the main house. After the crush, the fermentation process begins and typically arrives with the first spouts about dehydration from the more casual winery goers. At this time, guests are given their first of two full ladles of water and are urged to share with the livestock to aid in the drought and overhead costs.

Then, it's onto the aging process, where the wine is placed into specially crafted French oak barrels infused with a light and dark toast for four to eight years. Members of the Jessup Farms platinum membership are invited to stay on the property in multi-family quarters during the duration, where they'll work at the winery and receive a version of a wage.

Finally, visitors will rack, filter, and bottle the wine in a process overseen by Daddy Jessup and Mother Annabelle, allowing them to mingle with the guests and keep an eye on their product. During this culmination of years of meticulous attention to detail and grueling labor, visitors are asked to disrobe to their underwear to prevent contamination and the use of concealed bladders taped to the guests' legs. Unfortunately, this is a non-negotiable policy, and failure to comply will result in termination from the course and any outstanding debt or holiday plans. And as a magical day comes to a close, guests are required to submit to a breathtaking sunset roundup by ICE. Detainees will be treated to a complete, complementary, and shockingly thorough physical exam with transportation included.

Burcham Street Cellars

Set within the city of Sutton's charming Old District, in an industrial building built with bricks from the great Sutton fire of 1919, Burcham Street Cellars is an urban winery that fuses the fragrance of fermenting grapes with car exhaust, while offering a delicate play of neighboring construction and the full-bodied taste of waste management trucks twirling atop your tongue. Housed in a former sewing machine factory and infamous speakeasy called Chubby's—frequented by silent film stars Percy Quinn, Sterling Howard, and influential "lost generation" author Dorothy Beckert—Burcham Street Cellars offers something most urban wineries don't. It combines the phenomenon of a contemporary city winery with the traditional countryside vineyard winery, divided into two structures connected by the Burcham Street Cellars Skyway: The Metropolis and The Hamlet.

The Metropolis side of Burcham Street employs the latest technological advances in winemaking along with minimalistic, organic, and molecular gastronomical methods, particularly with their champion ice wine and pinot vapors. While the Hamlet, contrastingly, applies a more conventional, rural approach to processing wine and does so in a tongue-in-cheek fashion.

Amidst Sutton's lively old textile hub—now a campus-adjacent drag of nighttime bars, hookah lounges, and an air of desperation and tortilla chips—the Hamlet half of Burcham Street Cellars manufactures wine the old-fashioned way, sarcastically, enhancing the bit with dirt floors, indoor trees, and living walls of succulents and archaic farming tools. The viticulturists wear hip field clothes and spell their names traditionally for an added touch of kitschy heritage.

While back at the Metropolis, Burcham Street uses cutting-edge science to engineer a style of winemaking they describe as "chemical artistry" and "super different." In addition to both their ironic and all but conventional bottled wines, Burcham Street Cellars boasts their signature transglutaminase wine-pops comprised of flash-frozen grapes using liquid nitrogen, encased in a floral, caramelized gel with rock candy sticks—which took first place in 2017 at the Newport Adult Confectionery Competition and Car Show. Furthermore, their line of wine-infused vape flavors offers consumers a glass-less alternative to their red or white favorites, from classic Bordeaux varietals and Grenache to chardonnay and sweet vermouth, using naturally synthetic oils extracted from the must.

Moreover, visitors seeking an experience-within-an-experience can take in the independently operated Micro B.S. Cellars located inside the Metropolis. This micro-winery affiliate uses grapes sourced from Burcham Street Cellars through a rental agreement including intellectual property and the B.S. initials, making the entire Burcham Street Cellars operation a "Millennial meta mecca." Trademarked.

The Viniculture Institute of America

Just north of the Los Remos Wildlife Reserve in the St. Sebastian wine region, destination seekers will find the prestigious Viniculture Institute of America—the country's leading educator in grape cultivation for winemaking. The Institute's alumni include acclaimed Amish vintner Thax Bailer, who going against the abstinent ways of the Old Order, founded the Pennsylvania-set Laurel Ford Winery and Inn, with wedding venue and barn raising. Gillian Barnes, the self-proclaimed "San Diego Queen of Zinfandel," graduated from the world-renowned institute in '08 before her South Coast winery, Bernecino Oaks, received a platinum award for their semisweet-to-sweet 2014 White Zinfandel at the National Women's Club Wine Challenge; as well as a gold medal at the 2014 Gated-Community Tea Party March and Cake Walk. The apparent pride of the Institute, the now iconic, trendsetting Sawa twins, injected their expertise and North Coast education into the Japanese hills of Izu in 1993 when they built the Resort Palace Hotel Winery and Clothing Factory Outlet. In a celebrated partnership with Suzuka Tires, Cheryl and Kao Sawa revolutionized the industry with their rubber-made designer wine bottle and wine glass koozies.

Established in 1936 as the Placer Vintner Institute by mining tycoon, wine aficionado, and staunch gluttony advocator Cyrus Theodore Bloome, the school's vineyards and surrounding structures date back to the 1820s, when they were founded as a Spanish mission by Father Pedro Ortega. Sitting at the site of the California birthplace for blessing grapes, the Viniculture Institute of America—as it came to be known in 1950—like the monks and priests of its predecessor, the students take a vow of silence—a tradition steeped in the sacred soil for nearly two hundred years. They're required to disown any worldly possessions and inheritances after tuition, which is required in full before orientation. Celibacy is asked of but not enforced, given the continual flow of wine—although it must be silent and free of mutual climax as stated under the old and new Catholic law.

As part of their training, students at the institute cultivate grapes and produce wine varieties for sale under the school's illustrious and award-winning label. Visitors to the winery are invited to sample the student's creations and partake in the college's 3-star restaurant with meal plan and hot bar, alongside daily pairing presentations. From patties and nuggets to sticks and loaves, the institute's knowledgeable students match their acclaimed seven-varietal blends, hyper-grapes, and mega-wines with the perfect mouthwatering morsels. Guests are well advised to stop by the school store to pick up a copy of the institute's best-selling coffee table book, highlighting its origins, contributions to the industry, and, most importantly, love letters to its wealthiest donors.

Autumn Leaves: A Behind-the-Scenes Look

A *s life fades…so do autumn leaves.*

Hey, everybody! Matt Segal, here. Art Director, Funeral Unit, on *Autumn Leaves*. We hope you're enjoying this special edition *Autumn Leaves* season fifty-one DVD set. There's something special about working on one of America's most beloved and longest-running soap operas. That's why we'd like to offer you a behind-the-scenes look at our side of the production and hopefully provide you with a little insight into what it is we all do around here anyway. Follow me!

Funerals are the backbone of American soap operas. So, when doing a show about the interwoven relationships of a bunch of wealthy geriatrics so close to the end, you're going to get a lot of funerals. That's why the art department's funeral unit is without question one of the key components in the success of *Autumn Leaves*. The show's nerve center. That's a little joke we have in-house. Always breaks people up. With an average of twenty funerals per week, our fantastic writers certainly keep us busy. In fact, this year, we hit thirty-two—an *Autumn Leaves* record. That's roughly six-and-half funerals for each day of a production week. In an hour-long format, that's a little over one funeral every ten minutes. So, with ads, you're lookin' at a funeral-to-non-funeral ratio of something like three to one. I've got the exact figure written down somewhere in my car. So, you can imagine our hands stay pretty full. Not to mention ice cold. I'm kidding, of course. I'm not a writer per se, but I dabble in treatments here and there. I've actually been working on a few storylines. I've got this one about an evil twin that has a scar and wears an eye patch. Maybe he's been out to sea for a long time or wears a leather jacket and sits outside a gymnasium at night on a parked motorcycle. I'm still kicking it around. Maybe I'll bring it up the next time we all go out for drinks, and I have to follow everybody then make up an excuse for running into them.

Now, it's no industry secret *Autumn Leaves* also sees its fair share of hospital beds each week. They don't all go as suddenly as Jack Tabernacle on the shuffleboard court mid-coitus. And although the hospital unit claims they're more vital to the show's longevity, we here on the side of the eternal know those vegetables wouldn't have a pulse without Ivan from sound. Beep...Beep...Beep. Yes, it's true, they are a critical part of the show. "Critical," get it? *sound of crickets* Damnit, Ivan! Yes, it's a feud as old as the genre itself and as common as an extramarital affair with a coma patient. We keep things pretty friendly, though. Sure, there may be the occasional devastating humiliation, neighborly assault, or devastating humiliation, but it's all in good humor.

There was this one-time last season when we defecated in all their bedpans before shooting. Haha, it was a riot. They got us back pretty good, though, when they filled one of our caskets with fish slurry. The crew had to bring out the squeegees for that one. Let's just say the viewing of *Autumn Leaves* fan-favorite Gloria Smite wasn't limited to her cherry poplar casket, if you know what I mean. Or the time they replaced our candles for the memorial service of Estelle Goth with a bunch of no-light, trick candles. Which, if you ask me, is an odd market for processional candles. Oh, but we got even by blackmailing one of the more timid showrunners into offering some of the one-off candy strippers leading roles on the show, then had them take it back after everybody called their friends and family. We all cracked up—even some of the hospital gang. Yup, there's nothing like some good ole fashioned on-set hijinks to keep up morale and bring us all closer together. We're kinda like grade school kids who show affection by picking on each other, which sometimes results in termination or the threat of jail time. Fun factoid: Sometimes we like to join forces and gang up on the Wedding Unit. They're such easy targets. So hopeful with heads in the clouds. I think it's being around all that white. The other day we bribed our pink-haired set dresser Kiko with tickets to the ice cream museum to switch out the rings for Angela's wedding with a pair of chrome cock rings. Melody McDonald, who plays

Angela, got two fingers in before we just lost it. After shooting, we buried the hatchet with some flour and sugar, so it was all good.

Because at the end of the day, we're like a big family around here. A big family made up of smaller families. Like the Dillard family from Salt Lake back in season forty-nine—the one with four breakfasts and a strict sleeping schedule. I kind of fancy myself the dad of our funeral family. You know, I wanted to print up some T-shirts with that written across the chest, but I couldn't find a printing company that would do it. And as the dad of the funeral unit here on *Autumn Leaves*, it's my job to bring these bleak affairs to life. Hey, that's not bad. I should write that one down. It's a task I couldn't do without the help of a lot of really talented people. The ones responsible for the lion's share of this whole operation. Come on; I'll introduce you!

It's kind of crazy around here right now. Everybody's prepping for the big funeral of Dale Quinn, a beloved member of *Autumn Leaves*, who was killed in episode 137, season forty-eight, then resurrected the following year by a park gypsy. This time around, though, he took his grandson with him. Spoiler alert. It's a twofer, so there's a lot of excitement on set! Train enthusiast and double-retired heart surgeon—pun—Dale Quinn was taking his grandson Eddie out for a spin on his new motorcycle and sidecar when he went straight through the front window of a hobby store. And during a half-off carving foam sale, so the place was packed. Yes, foam; foam which would have cushioned their impact and saved their lives had the display not been moved to the back of the store in order to promote a new line of quick-drying adhesives. Now, that's not in the episode, but I mentioned it to the writers as a possibility. And they said...Well, never mind what they said. But they were extremely animated. I think I'm wearin' 'em down!

Now, I should confess something...Frankly, between you and me—here, come in close—see the child actor playing Eddie? I couldn't be happier to see that kid in a box. I shouldn't say anything, I know, I don't wanna get anyone in trouble, but the other morning, he stole by turnover. He just stared at me while he ate it, laughing. He seemed to take great pleasure in it, too—rocking back and forth. Then again, that could have just been the sugar. It's OK; one of the trainers distracted him yesterday with a cat on-set playing an emotional support animal, while I snuck into his dressing room and changed all the answers on his homework. Great cat! Very professional.

Over there by craft services is Jimmy, our lead painter. A master of burgundies and blacks. The rainy outdoor funeral of Mayor Dean Holbrook in season fifty—Jimmy was responsible for the dreary backdrop painting, which was inspired interestingly enough by a Petaluma pet cemetery, with foliage accents taken from a field outside a prominent tri-state prison crematorium. You'll probably remember that piece got plenty of attention on social media because a lot of viewers thought they saw the ghost of Dean's campaign double and former lover in the distance peering out from behind a tree. You *Autumn Leaves* theorists are going to love this next bit...Because Jimmy and I never discussed adding anything like that beforehand, and I've questioned him on this in the past because I don't see— I don't see very well at all— But he's always skirted around the subject.

Maybe today, we can get some real answers out of him. Looks like he's got his hands full with that lasagna, though. Really seems to be pushing the limits of that plate. And it's a corner piece, so you know it's solid and packing some heft— Oh, there it goes! That's, that's embarrassing; we better not bother him. Just look away. Look away. Super dude, though! Super dude.

With script supervisor Allen Gaglione, it's our veteran set decorator Sam Weisman with the shaved head. A legend in soap opera funerals, as well as a genius with candelabras and crushed velvet. Sam is really the lifeblood of everything you see here; and has been for decades—the arrangements, the four pews of two, even the casket placement. Before Weisman, nobody in town was putting the casket at the front of the church. Or centered. They really revolutionized the game.

And that's our prop master, Doug Atkins, chatting it up with camera operator Skip Calderon at the pulpit. He's the one that made the crucifix used by Monsignor Mahoney and that unnamed priest from the old country during the quickie-exorcism of Demon Ashly at the Gloria Mayweather funeral. Along with the pea soup projectile that covered the front row like a Gallagher show. He also whipped up the ectoplasm of Dona Goldstein's spirit from Rose's catered séance in season forty-seven. He even fashioned together Lawrence Wilcox's iconic double-wide casket last year. Lawrence Wilcox—the highly regarded *Autumn Leaves* city councilman with the catchphrase "Spread out!" Doug also did Ralph Stokes's funeral and the Stokes family casket after they were bumped off at their Outer Banks beach house, which you long-time viewers remember was shaped like a four-finger cigar case. Sixty gauge, if I'm not mistaken. That was a bit before my time.

I'll tell ya this…It's one thing to have a vision; it's another thing to execute that vision. And I couldn't be more appreciative of this hard-working bunch behind me. I try to make all the services on *Autumn Leaves* different. You know, give them each their own feel. Their own essence. Unique to the specific tone of each episode. And thankfully, the truth of it is, when you're working with a wellspring of material placed in the hands of both industry greats and a new wave of fresh, up-and-coming television mortuary talents, you know the *Autumn Leaves* magic will be sustainable for years and years to come.

Well, I should probably get back to work. Whaddya think I do all day, horse around and make videos? We hope you've enjoyed this short behind-the-scenes featurette on *Autumn Leaves* and a look at its funeral unit. Now, whaddya say we get back to the show?

Hey, look! There's head writer Susan Blackmore. I'd love to get her take on this episode I'm writing about a little girl trapped in a well under the bandstand during a Fourth of July celebration. Or this other one!— Don't go yet— About Clementine Jacobs and Guinevere Turnstile held up in Maxwell's cabin after killing their husbands in a not-so-playful pact made over boxed wine and drunk bacon. Or!— Stay with me!— Ned's trip to a fortune teller. Or a carnival. His nephew, a bad seed, schmoozes the widow Clayton for her inheritance— You keep trying to walk away— A heatwave! Lucy kidnapping Mark's baby. A storm! Famine! Locus! Hey! Maybe you could write into the show and request some of my storylines. You'd be doing me a favor. Hey, wait! Where ya goin'?!

The Four-Bed, Three-Bath Sedan

*W*hile sitting in my dermatologist's reception waiting for my name to be drawn from what I had convinced myself at the time was a large, possibly gaudy raffle drum, after growing tired of mentally arranging my fellow three o'clock-ers by the height of their pants tents—which I believe I eyed with a surprising level of accuracy—I began thumbing through an especially outdated automotive magazine called *Roving Marvels*. It was one of those typical luxury car periodicals full of flashy prototypes, high-performance sports cars, and six-figure price tags concealed tastefully within the fanciful narratives accompanying each vehicle in a fashion similar to a manufacturer's catalog. Like the ones you put out for company. These starry-eyed projections were painted with glamourous brush strokes and were rather keen on placing the reader in a whimsically charged and equally boastful evening out with the kind of friends or spouse nobody has. But, if one did, say for the sake of argument, they would in all likelihood be described as elegant and carefree. But not as elegant and carefree as you would be if you owned such a fine and luxurious automobile. Carmakers would have you believe that being free of something, such as care, isn't necessarily absolute. Not when you have the option for an eight-thousand-dollar racing strip.

Nevertheless, while leafing through this oddly faded and unsettlingly stained April '05 edition—which was strangely addressed to a "Mr. Diane Porcelain"—I was struck by a centerfold headline so enthralling I trembled in the wake of its notion, while at the same time jumping into the lead of the pants tent competition. Which I didn't realize was a competition until I was winning. "By Greenwald Motors," it read in a simple yet powerful font, "The Four-Bed, Three-Bath Sedan." Mesmerized by breathtaking images of stylish tapestries and golden fixtures—as well as a shockingly ergonomic layout, specifically the sunken living room behind the driver's seat, flanked by the brilliantly designed study and comfortably spacious den with mini fireplace—I was immediately filled with virility, followed by a feeling of immense shame. Not just for my years of encouraging the automotive industry with the purchase of inferior design after inferior design and the once now seemingly joyless ride in the backseat of a Tacoma—which at the time, I happily registered with an online motor forum just to rave about—but also for my vain naivety. How had this glorious creation remained a mystery to me for so long? Trapped for decades, screaming, and flailing wildly within the cushy, sometimes hollow confines of my mental prison, spending my better years in an undeniably meaningless and rash-covered existence, I was suddenly blessed with a vehement sense of steadfast purpose. Love, family, death—it all meant nothing to me now. Six simple words that made my head reel, disabling it with a dizzying flurry of strikingly picturesque images. I could see it all so clearly. Everyone looked so elegant and carefree.

"A toast! To extravagance and excess! Bobby, be a sack of loveliness and close the sliding door; we're driving through a rough neighborhood. Who wants tapas?!"

Still trembling from my cognitive revelation, I extended the pages of what was slowly revealing itself to me as a centerfold retrospective from the 1960s, bringing to light a world in balance. Splendor packed harmoniously behind four unassuming Tudor doors with rounded stained-glass windows and a welcome mat that extended from under the driver-side door. Suddenly my senses became one. My spirit took over. I began channeling nourishment throughout my body in the form of pure energy. I had risen to the highest level of awareness. My body, no longer operational, sat there in the lobby sobbing at the sight of magnificent. I could sense a feeling of unease fill the reception as the other patients diverted their attention from my weeping shell. They lifted their phones and faked interest in the carpet runs beneath their feet.

After consciousness returned, I tasked myself with learning everything there was to know about this truly roving marvel. I was unfamiliar with Greenwald Motors but was resolute in my commitment. Who was the automotive genius behind this divine construction? How did it come to fruition? And most curiously, how

163

well does sound travel throughout the car in the event there's a call for a nursery? After eight painstaking months of research, which included several expensive trips to the National Archives in D.C.—due in part to my weakness for flashy souvenirs and a palate easily seduced by steamed foods served from a cart—I was able to put together a detailed account of the man behind this holiest of holy midsize creations and its sacred journey from inception to showroom. I present my findings in the following:

1907: Ellis Eugen Grunwald enters the world in steerage to German immigrants arriving in New York Harbor. His mother carries him under her arm and is charged for an extra bag. His father is stricken with typhoid but insists his synonyms are from the gruel, which he maintains was undercooked. The family's name becomes Greenwald after an official's spelling error due chiefly to Mr. Grunwald's complexion.

1917: At age ten, Ellis exhibits an early interest in design by sprucing up the family's Lower East Side apartment with fabrics that aren't shades of beige or grey. That same year, Ellis reads *The Art of Feng Shui* by Zhang Tao Li and rearranges the family living room to maximize comfort and the flow of Qi, especially around the toilet.

1918: Ellis's father moves the family to the Midwest and finds employment on the factory floor of the Federal Rail Toboggan Company, an early manufacturer of roller coaster cars. He's posted at the assembly line as a roving replacement for sickly workers who pass out and learns the true meaning of American efficiency.

1921-1924: Ellis attends Pearl Ward High School in Michigan, where he perfects the butt-cut and wearing collars outside of sweaters. He excels in shop and geometry, expanding his awareness of space and basic engineering. He works nights at the coaster car factory and relieves his father's post each evening. Everything is hunky-dory.

1925: Ellis wins the National Junior Metal Kit Contest sponsored by Build Co. Toys and is awarded a scholarship to Chicago's Institute of Architecture and Design. The next day, his father keels over at work and dies. Ellis fills his spot on the assembly line and grieves productively. Indigent, Ellis is forced to put off school and work at the factory full-time to provide for his mother. She shows her gratitude by pinching his cheek when he comes home and tells him he's a good boy.

1926-1928: Ellis loses himself in the work and is promoted to line foreman. In two years, he goes from the factory floor to concept design, with a short detour through personnel administration—a department focused on worker grievances and safety. It operates under soft business hours.

1929: Ellis is the assistant lead designer for the Federal Rail Toboggan Company and finds success with his first two car designs: the not entirely square coaster cars for the Gravity Scenic Railway at Lakeview Gardens in New York, which he equips with ashtrays and a plaid pull-out blanket in lieu of lap bar; as well as the rocket-shaped cars for the lunar-themed Dive-The-Dip ride at Gracehill Park in Ohio, that he fashions with a hat rack and collapsible drink tables.

1931: Ellis builds relationships with investors who quickly take notice of his gumption and eye for sumptuousness. At age twenty-four, he partners with a former developer from the Admiral Motor Company, Norbert O'Shea, and forms his own company, the Ellis Greenwald Company. Several investors back him: Teddy Barton, a canvas baron from Philadelphia; Barton's squash instructor and mistress; and her husband, Otis Donnelly, a stockholder in the American Entertainment Company—prominent architects of early amusement parks. Ellis and his team aim to make the first-ever rail-less coaster car for street use. They call it the Greenwald Spinny Derby. Passengers sit in an upside-down bowler that spins clockwise. It is terribly difficult to drive in a straight line and results in numerous accidents, wrong turns, and queasy motorists.

1932: Ellis sets out to build a proper automobile, funded in part by a contract with the Soviet Union to purchase eight million dollars worth of Spinny Derbys sight unseen. Ellis learns the true potential of American cachet. The Greenwald Type-2 boasts a 3.6-liter V8 engine and elegant curtains with hand ticking by designer and cloth master Gustavo Hail. The public takes notice of the Greenwald name and recognizes their attention to detail and emphasis on extravagance.

1933: The Ellis Greenwald Company is hit hard by the Depression and lays off thousands of workers. At Christmas time, Ellis gifts hundreds of families a twelve-yard roll of Italian leather and a case of saddle oil.

1934: Ellis wakes from a dream and sketches a Prairie-style inspired house with four wheels and conservatory. He is baffled by his vision but holds firmly to the image. He keeps the sketch locked away in his office inside a steel safe lifted from the sidewalk while next to a hanging piano and a pair of window washers in comedic distress.

1935: The Ellis Greenwald Company rolls out their third automobile: the '35 Greenwald Business Budget Sedan—an inexpensive, two-door hardtop with standard and deluxe trim options. They partner with Byline Foods and run one of the automotive industry's first national promotions, offering buyers a year's supply of canned creamed chipped beef and a limited-edition darning egg.

1937: With the help of engine designer Felix Goosen, the Ellis Greenwald Company builds a 4.6-liter, 6-cylinder roadster called The Tingler and wins the prestigious 24 hours of Duchamp on the historic Castra-Martin street circuit. The Tingler has a torpedo-shaped chassis and a coup glass dispenser for victory champaign.

1939: After bringing on more investors and building several new factories, the Ellis Greenwald Company becomes Greenwald Motors. They adjust the green of the signature Greenwald logo by two points and are heralded by the public for their bold rebranding.

1941-1944: Greenwald Motors dives into the war effort and builds three military vehicles for the U.S. Government. Firstly, there's the rugged yet harmoniously constructed Greenwald Mandarin Duck, an all-wheel-drive amphibious vehicle with mounted guns and red satin upholstery, inspired by the Chinese prints from Ellis's youth. After several tours in the Pacific, they prove too slow and lavish for combat. Internally, Japanese troops refer to the destruction of these vehicles as "duck soup." Secondly, a motorcycle and sidecar outfit called the

Greenwald TR-82 that comes in both jungle and desert finishes. The motorcycle frames are outsourced to Winton Motor Works, who dissolve shortly after production begins, leaving the regiments of the 9th Infantry Division with two thousand stationary sidecars waiting for them on the shores of the Baltic Sea. The Germans later commandeer the sidecars and, after taking a page from other Axis powers, fashion them into utility rickshaws. Finally, there is the armored, 4x4 MT7 Jeep, nicknamed the "Tyke." It has heavy but fashionable canvas doors to protect against heavy arms fire and a retractable mesh tarpaulin for nice days. The MT7 plays a strategic role for British soldiers in the Italian invasion of Egypt by providing them shelter underneath the chassis and warmth next to the radiators.

1946: Greenwald Motors flourishes amid postwar prosperity and beats its competitors to the production line. They introduce the iconic 1946 Greenwald Leisure Coupe fitted with their newly designed streamline V8 engine and back window shelving for a small, private library and accent pieces. Automotive historians later regard such pieces as a predecessor to the dashboard ornament, particularly the famous hip-swiveling Hula Hoop Hattie Doll, which emerged during the war—a spring-encased plastic bomber girl in culottes with a hula hoop, invented, of course, by toy tycoon Andrew Alhulahoopé. The Leisure Coupe is the first Greenwald automobile to be crash-tested, revolutionizing the industry and public safety. Human cadavers serve as early test subjects but soon fall under labor union violations following the ruling from The North American Workers of the Hereafter vs. Greenwald Motors. Ellis employs the first-ever crash test dummy, named Windshield Willie, designed by Greenwald engineer Wallace Murphy. Windshield Willie is adopted by the National Institute of Standards and Technology and later serves on the board of the United Test Subjects of America.

1949: Ellis designs and builds a twenty-nine thousand square foot house in Westminster, Illinois, just outside Chicago. The home features an open, U-shaped layout focused on unity reinforced by geometry and natural light. It has a double-wide porte-cochère supporting a second-story veranda, and in the back, a lily pond with swan-shaped paddleboats and a tunnel of love.

1951: Ellis Greenwald tackles his most ambitious automobile to date: The Divorcee—a cozy, Uptown-apartment-like four-door station wagon with swivel seats, a hideaway bed, and a kitchenette with wet bar. It provides comfortable elegance for the newly independent man with nothing ahead of him but the open road and rest stop showers.

1953: Ellis attends a national trailer show in California and is enthralled by the displays and their use of mobile hospitalities, both basic and luxury. He is also taken by a trade show model by the name of Gloria Estabrook, diving from a springboard into a large pool in the middle of the showroom floor. They marry three weeks later in a mobile chapel prototype constructed by Greenwald Motors for early streamlining of the Las Vegas marriage process.

1954-1955: Ellis begins preliminary concept work on a one thousand plus horsepower, V12 multi-room sedan. He consults with engine builders and interior designers alike. A prototype for a two-bed plus den proves successful but provides little room for entertaining. A second prototype incorporates a split-foyer with a bonus room and easy access to the engine via a linen closet in the basement next to the laundry room. Unfortunately, the recently proposed Federal-Aid Highway Act, implementing a network of overpasses country-wide, limits the vertical clearance of vehicles to fourteen feet.

1957: Ellis travels to India and the Far East in search of exotic textiles. He returns with plush fabrics, ornate rugs, and a smell he can't get out of his clothes. His team of interior designers experiment with unconventional layouts and make groundbreaking innovations in space management. His in-house decorators work closely with lead furniture designer Anne Hoffman to complement a mid-century modern aesthetic and geometrical build. It's a creative roundtable of philosophies focusing on a balanced use of ornament and function. Ellis requests gold-plated light switch covers and more shag.

1958: Greenwald Motors partners with Mitchell-Myers Construction and Siding for what Ellis Greenwald promises will be the most luxurious and magnificent production automobile the world has ever seen.

1960: The Greenwald Four-Bed, Three-Bath Sedan is unveiled at the American National Auto Show in Detroit on January 11, 1960. Ellis Greenwald makes a special appearance and acknowledges the crowd after exiting the automobile with his wife and a tray of cookies straight from the oven. Attendees are given a brief tour and asked to remove their hats upon entry. It is a marvel of highway travel but is tight in the city. Some of its features include crown molding with ornate detailing, decadent light fixtures, a four-burner stove, sewing room, alternator, central heating, and a separate doorbell-horn function. Its free-flowing interior provides ideal space for long road trips and hosting out-of-town guests, as well as roaming key parties. Public reception is positive, and Greenwald Motors places more than two hundred pre-orders from showgoers. A down payment secures buyers a special edition limited production Sebastian Taylor bedroom suite with a pair of alabaster lamps and a jewel-encrusted music box.

1961: Greenwald Motors retrofits their assembly lines with cylindrical robots featuring five axes of freedom, allowing for faster production, greater profit, and fewer sick days during the World Series. The Greenwald Four-Bed, Three-Bath Sedan goes into production.

1962: Greenwald's competitors react to the multi-room sedan and follow suit with their own builds. Under the Elf Automotive Group, German automaker Sieben introduces a two-door, double-bed, rear-engine economy coupe called the Sieben Barracks. They're popular with North American youth and führers in hiding. There's the Australian 1962 Beach Auto-Bungalow by the Arvo Motors and Engineering Company, which features a flatbed porch with screened-in and surfboard rack options. It's marketed as a fun, leisure vehicle perfect for summer outings, holidays, and weekend getaways with your sidepiece. In Japan, Nakiri Motors unveils a three-bed, traditional Japanese-style four-door with large rooms, railed ceilings, and a lifespan of four hundred thousand miles.

1963: The Greenwald Four-Bed sells just two thousand units in its first year after Greenwald Motors invests nearly half a billion dollars in its production. It is an underwhelming and puzzling start to a grand and ambitious undertaking. Ellis and his team design and engineer two special edition four-beds with slight modifications to each. The first comes with pea green and saffron schemed interior with flower wallpaper and ambiguous art; the second echoes a chic Manhattan apartment with black and white decor, a baby grand piano, and ambiguous art.

1964: Sales continue to struggle. An increase in building materials—e.g., roofing shingles and gutters, due to unusually excessive rainfall and a redesigned camshaft following poor chimney placement—leads to costs overrun and a thirty-seven percent markup on all Greenwald multi-room sedans. The grandiose and lavish notion of a spacious multiroom automobile proves impractical in a time of confusion and growing tensions.

1966-1968: Ellis Greenwald doubles down. He spends two years sketching and designing a multi-wing, five-axle, all-wheel-drive sedan with a glass atrium and rose garden. It has six bedrooms, four and a half baths, and a pool at the boot of the car. The blueprints alone send Greenwald Motors into bankruptcy.

1971-1973: In response to the growing number of German and Japanese compact and subcompact imports shifting the U.S. auto market, Greenwald Motors scales back production of their multiroom sedans. They introduce a sensible, two-door, four-seat, front-engine hatchback called the Greenwald Moth and are lambasted by critics for a less than lavish design with zero amenities.

1974: Greenwald Motors dissolves in the wake of the oil crisis. The lot of their multiroom chassis are donated and shipped to homeless organizations throughout the country. The homeless live in the stationary, four-bedroom automobile frames with functioning utilities. It is a sad byproduct of the times. From their windows, they watch the daily commute of motorists and the queues outside gas stations and are thankful for what they have.

1981: At age seventy-four, Ellis Greenwald develops a pulmonary disease and passes in his sleep at his Beaver Mill home in western Pennsylvania. He is interred in the Loughery-Lane Cemetery in Upstate New York following a funeral procession of multiroom Greenwald automobiles. His body is displayed in the breakfast nook of a four-bed, three-bath sedan, dressed in his favorite robe and given a smoking pipe and newspaper.

Francis Goes Back

*I*n 1981, filmmaker Leslie Peters joined legendary funnyman and television icon Francis O'Donnell on his trip back home to New Bridgeburg, Connecticut, for the first time in over thirty years. O'Donnell broke onto the comedy club scene in the early 1960s before landing a job on the writing staff of The Milligan Sisters Variety Hour. There, he made his television acting debut and by the early 1970s had risen to sitcom super-stardom with The Francis O'Donnell Show, impersonating and joking his way into the hearts of Americans everywhere. Peters's now celebrated hour-long TV special highlights the comedian's roots and showcases his more affectionate and sentimental side, a side rarely seen by audiences. Francis Goes Back is an intimate portrait of a comic, a writer, an actor, a director, an innovator, and a man. The following is a reading of the film's transcript, with state-of-the-art audio reconstruction:

[birds chirping]

[gentle wind]

[sound of an old car on a dirt road]

Francis: I think New England is just about the prettiest, most perfect place a kid could come from and call home. Especially in autumn, which is a word only New Englanders can use. This place...it, uh, it stirs up a kind of nostalgia. As is the sensation I think most have when returning home. A longing for when things were, uh, not necessarily simpler, but certainly less complicated. A time without portable cassette players and cable converter boxes. You ever try to use one of those? Like a damn Rubik's Cube, which is basically a dollar ninety-nine version of twiddling your thumbs. Are they a sponsor? Oh boy, we're gonna get some mail for that one. Things and people go at a different pace around here. There's a kind of comfort and serenity in that. I'm hopeful that what will come of this journey into the past is, uh, well, a recharge for one, something to get me through my third act. And, uh, I'm expecting a humbling experience, a reminder. I think we all need the occasional reminder of where we're from. Often, I think, will it hold the answers to where we're going. It's important to remember why we made the decisions we made—the catalyst for our dreams. That reminds me of the old McMillan and Sons Funeral Parlor slogan. Except they'd say, "the *Cadillac* for *your* dreams." They sold this beauty of a coffin. It was silver with detailing. Looked like a fancy bullet. Or some kind o' regal soapbox car. Oh, how we loved our derbies. Leslie, maybe there, show me as a kid in an oversized bowler, the brim resting on my nose. Maybe with a slow push-in. That'd be funny.

[car rattling]

Francis: Speaking of cars...this is a 1958 Ford Edsel. Anybody who knows cars knows that the Edsel name is synonymous with success and luxury. See the toilet seat grille on the front? Also, kind of looks like a vagina, so you know right away there's something magical under the hood. I'll never forget the day my father brought it home. He had the biggest smile on his face. He was so proud of this car. It was a testament to his hard work and a man's God-given right to make a foolish purchase based solely on marketing hype. In the driveway, I remember I pulled down my pants and stuck my butt to the grille and requested some privacy. What I wouldn't do for a laugh in those days. Had I known Stacey Sutton was having her birthday party across the street, I may have chosen a less revealing form of jest. She was my best friend growing up. Actually, I carried quite the touch for Stacey. I was deeply, profoundly in love with that woman. We were eight years old. We would walk along this road in the summertime pretending our car had broken down and we were late for a dinner party in the city, a fundraiser. I remember I bought her this giant diamond ring from Grover Schwartz for two bits. It was his mother's. He told his parents it was stolen and blamed it on a drifter that had just started work as a bagboy at the Penny 'N' Save and was, you know, getting his life back together. Ah, we were crazy back then.

[car struggling]

Francis: Yep, this old thing brings back a lot of memories: I learned to drive in this car; went to my first drive-in theater in this car; learned how to cut through a bra strap in that backseat there, which I could have sworn was tan. Actually, you know, uh, now that I, now that I think about it...Wait, yeah, no, uh, I'm sorry, our first car was an Airflow. That's right, a Chrysler Airflow. My old man lost it pitching pennies out behind the barbershop after like a week from driving it off the lot. I had never seen that look on my mother's face before. It was as if she was thinking, *I could have done better.* Then, that means— Huh. You know, uh, I'm not entirely sure where this car came from. Leslie, do we know where this car came from? What are you— What are you signaling? Why are you waving? I feel like you're trying to tell me something. No, I don't understand what you're saying. You keep doing that with your hand; I don't know what that means! Well, it's distracting. Anyway, about five miles up the road here is the quaint little town of New Bridgeburg, Connecticut. That's where I was born. And that's where I grew up. Come on, whaddya say, let's take a trip down memory boulevard.

[heartwarming orchestral music]

[sounds of traffic]

Francis: Now, this is the main thoroughfare and downtown New Bridgeburg. Every Easter we'd wake up early to stake out the best spot to view the parade. They stopped running that in '53 after one of the floats caught fire. All that fur and fake grass—woosh—went right up in flames. Same thing happened at the egg hunt. Now, it's hard to tell

177

if the eggs were incendiary by design or if it was, you know, some sort of fluke down at the farm. Now, the Christmas parade...Oh, that was a magical time. Wreaths and bows on all the lampposts and lights strung over the road here. We waited all year for that parade because that meant Christmas had come. We would stand out here in the cold for hours just to see Santa. And I was a susceptible kid, you know, impressionable; I bought the whole Santa thing hook, line, and sinker. In those days, Santa was played by a man named Rafe Fletcher. Worked at the lighting and ceiling fan shop back behind us a couple of blocks. And his son, uh...now I believe his name was Doug...took over the gig after him. And then Doug's son after him. It was a Santa Claus dynasty. And at that time, the Fletchers were known around town as a family of lushes. You know, drunks. And one year, I'll never forget it...Rafe tied one on pretty good before the parade, and in the middle of it, he stood up, pulled down his pants, and peed off the side of the float. It hit me square in the forehead. I was nine years old, and Santa publicly peed on my face. Oh, it ruined Christmas that year. Next several, if my memory serves me well.

[car rattling]

Francis: Now, up here on the left, that was the music shop. And on the corner here at the video rental, that used to be, that used to be Skippy's Soda Shop. I took Mildred Wachowski there after the eighth-grade formal, and we had a butter whip sundae with six cups of black coffee. She wore this beautiful blue dress with little yellow flowers all over it. I remember it because, at one point, I sneezed and tried holding it back, and a small bead of mucus launched from my mouth and landed on her dress. She didn't see it, but I couldn't stop staring at that tiny damp spot on her chest. Of course, she noticed my gazes and, you know, took them the wrong way. Which is funny because I later learned that night after I walked her home, she met up with Mitchie Arnold and they necked because his sister died. And down that street is the old roller rink...across from the new roller rink.

[car honking]

[indiscernible insult]

Francis: Yeah, same to you, pal! Can you believe that guy? What does he know about ratings? [shouting] Yeah, maybe if we shared a marital bed! Leslie, use the second one...unless the first one's better. Well, you have both.

[car engine struggling]

Francis: And over here was Cooper's Hardware. Well, howdya like that, Cooper's is still here! This was my first job. I was twelve years old and would come in after school. I'd sweep the floor, take out the trash, arrange the nuts and bolts by their metallic hue. You know, little odd jobs like that. I'd get home around eleven after everybody was asleep and usually fry myself a Spam sandwich. It was nice. We had fun. Let's pull over here...I wanna stop for a second and go inside. I wanna see how much it's changed.

[car brakes squeaking]

Francis: Look at this...all this is new...the hedge and planters, sidewalk too. Used to just be a sort of thickness of cigarette filters and war propaganda leaflets everybody merely perceived as a pathway.

[door opening]

[bell chiming]

Francis: Oh, wow, it still has that smell. Like the Tin Man smoking wood dust from a plastic pipe. You know what I mean? You can taste it through your nose.

[footsteps shuffling]

Cooper: Little Francis O'Donnell...I don't believe it.

Francis: Is that who I think it is?

Cooper: Well, this is a treat; Mister fancy britches has returned to our sleepy little— What was that you called it on your show? "A rube incubator?"

Francis: [laughter] America, I'd like you to meet Mr. Don Cooper, one of those great, salt of the earth New Bridgeburg characters I remember so fondly. Mr. Cooper, tell the folks back home when you opened the doors to this—

Cooper: [impersonating] "I had this boss. My first boss actually. He smelled of fermented fish and open sores. And let's not forget his odors."

Francis: [hesitant laughter] Mr. Cooper's sense of humor is what made him so likable around town. What was that one you had about the dairy cow in stripes—

Cooper: "The constant smell of pickled fish wafting throughout the store gave it its indistinguishable charm."

Francis: [nervous laughter] Ya got it memorized and everything. You know, I seem to recall reading an article in last month's digest about the health benefits of fish. Did you see that? Really, it's a miracle food. I'm eating it three meals a day. Sometimes for a snack.

Cooper: "It was as if a military field infirmary started selling overpriced hammers and burnt popcorn."

Francis: I see you moved the plungers.

Cooper: "I mean, this fat piece of s*** was so revolting—"

Francis: Yeah, well, I think we got everything we needed.

Cooper: "—when he blew on his coffee, it curdled the milk!"

Francis: He's teasing. I-I-I don't do coffee jokes.

Cooper: Well, that's what you said, isn't it? On one of your records? In fact, I think I have the very record right here behind the counter all cued up. You want I should play it for your viewing audience?

Francis: Oh, I don't want to bore everybody with my past. That's…that's not why we're here. No, we're looking to see New Bridgeburg in the now. Moving forward. Leaving the past where it belongs. Behind a counter with noticeably visible rust.

Cooper: Gimme that camera! [struggling] I haven't had a customer in twenty f****** years. [microphone feedback] You destroyed my livelihood!

Francis: Look out, he's got an ax handle!

[light bulbs shattering]

[struggling and indiscernible dialogue]

Cooper: They put sardines in my mailbox!

Francis: He's going for the keys! Get down!

[keys hitting the ground]

Cooper: Do not duplicate! Do not duplicate!

[keys pinging off surfaces]

Francis: Stay down! Everybody, crawl to the car! Protect your eyes!

[bell chiming]

[bell chiming]

[bell chiming]

[car engine starting]

[car accelerating]

Francis: So, I worked there until...I wanna say my...Yeah, my junior year of high school. Oh, look, the A&C Cafeteria's still here!

[commercial break]

[wind blowing through trees]

[heartwarming piano music]

Francis: In every man's past, you'll find a structure of such and such square footage with so many rooms, sturdy craftsmanship, and a feeling of belonging. A place he once called home. Well, this is mine. 54 Perennial Lane. This is where I grew up. Right behind me there in that little blue house with the big porch. Ah, I miss that porch. My old man and I would sit out there for hours having those classic father and son heart-to-hearts. Nonverbally, of course. My dad wasn't a big talker. Unless I had left a toy in his immediate path. I treasure those moments. I'm happy to see the maple tree's still here. Isn't that a magnificent tree? God, I love this house. Let's peek inside and see who's home.

[knocking]

[door opening]

Francis: Hello? Anybody home? It's Francis O'Donnell.

[children screaming]

Francis: Well, hello there, you must be Ethan? Robby? Cold shoulder, huh? Whaddya got in your hand there? Is that a sponge? That's kind of weird. Do you know who I am? He's a bashful little fella. Are your parents home? Did you know that I lived in this house when I was your age? We moved here when I was two years old. That was 1928. Do you know how long ago that was? Same ole song, huh? Settle in, folks, we're gonna be here for a while. Oh, but stick around, he's got a big number in the second half.

[distant arguing]

[heavy footsteps]

Mother: You're leaving?!

Boyfriend: That's right, I'm leaving!

Mother: So, you're just walking out?!

Boyfriend: That's what you do when you leave!

Mother: What are we supposed to do? How are we gonna get by?

Boyfriend: I'm sure that little business venture of yours upstairs will keep you afloat. Land ya a real thoroughbred.

Mother: Please, they just shut off the gas, and the doctor says Robby might need one of those back braces. How'm I gonna pay for that working at the diner? Doubles won't cover it.

Boyfriend: Then I'd make sure that thoroughbred c**** with a big purse. See ya around, kid. *(to Mother)* You're disgusting.

[footsteps off]

Mother: Oh, I-I'm disgusting?! Fine! Get the hell outta here! And you know something else, you're right...you'll never be these kids' father! Ya bum! Ya no good lousy bum!

Francis: "It's the Francis O'Donnell Show!"

Mother: What?

Francis: [whispering] Is this a bad time?

Mother: Who the hell are you?

Francis: I, uh— I'm Francis. O-O-O'Donnell?

Mother: Yeah, we already got a bible.

Francis: No, Francis O'Donnell. I've returned to New Bridgeburg to visit my childhood home.

Mother: You're the comedian?

Francis: That's me.

Mother: Yeah, they said you'd be by. Didn't you die five years ago?

Francis: [laughter] That's, uh— [whispering] Do you, do you need a moment?

Mother: Why do you keep whispering? Oh, yes, please excuse my appearance. I was out back tending the *tomahtoes.*

Francis: Yes, well...That's some pretty rich soil you got back there, if I recall. I remember Sunday afternoons in the vegetable garden with my mother. We used to—

[sound of lighter striking and cigarette smoking]

Mother: Say, does this thing pay anything? 'Cause I got bills. And this looks like a lot of equipment.

Francis: I'm sure we can set you up with some T-shirts from the studio store. Leslie, can we get this lovely family some T-shirts?

Mother: Yeah, I need cash—

Francis: Wow, would you look at this living room...

[heartwarming music]

Mother: Leslie, I'm a small. Write that down.

Francis: Boy, does this bring back memories. I haven't stepped foot in here in thirty-five— I don't know how many years. It looks exactly the same. Maybe, uh, maybe a few more exposed wires, but this is it. Is that a cable spool with carpet stapled to it? And there seems to be, uh— Is anyone else feeling nauseated? Nobody? I feel lightheaded. Leslie, do a slow pan here with old photos. Maybe the sound of a movie projector even though they're stills. Birthdays...my mother's bridge club nights...my original production of *Death by Cape: The Magician's Struggle*. The whole thing took place in his dressing room, and the family ate it up. Though after a three-week engagement in the living room with two shows on Saturday and Sunday, their laughter shifted to them saying, "That's funny." We used to sit right here on the floor and listen to the radio after dinner. Oh, it was a marvelous time. We'd listen until we giggled ourselves senseless. Arthur Peabody...*The Albertson's Lye Comedy Hour*...Chester Woodrow. And then at Christmas, we put the tree over here where the, uh, where the easy chair is—

[soft crying]

Mother: This was his favorite chair. He never left it once, the lazy bum. He ate all his meals right here. Leslie, get a shot of the butt groove. Really get in there tight.

Francis: As I was saying...we would gather around here and open presents in front of the fireplace. One year, I asked my parents for this spy pen that wrote in invisible ink. And it had this secret compartment that could hold a single match. All I got that year was a ream of onion skin paper. I've never been more confused in my entire life.

Mother: Last year, he got me a can of pink salmon. He had such a big heart.

[faint sound of the camera crew being sick]

Francis: And in here is the dining room. And that's the kitchen around the corner. My mother was a fantastic cook. She used to make this corned beef hash— [shouting over vomiting] I say she used to make this corned beef hash that was the saltiest thing you'd ever tasted. She'd serve it with two beat yolks, a bowl of buttered donuts, and an ashtray, then send me off to school. Once, they found me down the street on Magnolia, passed out in Evelyn Walker's yard with my heart racing. You see, Ethan— Where's Ethan? Ethan?! Ah! You startled me. Have you been standing behind me this whole time?

Mother: We think he has the autism.

Francis: I see. I was going to say that when I was your age, we didn't have Loco Berries or cinnamon flakes with magical characters all over the box. No, our food came in boxes covered with public service announcements. And every kitchen had a crowbar for breaking open the canisters. I believe I saw your family's in the front yard. By the plastic, sun-faded toddler toy and trash bag half-filled with rainwater. In case you or your mother were looking for it.

[sound of multiple footsteps]

Francis: Now, of course, our bedrooms were upstairs here. My parents' room was down the hall there. I probably went in there a total of two times. And my room— My room was over here by the bathroom. It was my sanctuary. It had this— What is this? A padlock? There's a padlock on my room. Who puts a padlock inside?

Mother: Yeah, sorry, that room is off-limits. *(to Ethan)* Isn't it, sweetie?

Francis: Off-limits? This is my old room!

Mother: Yeah, well, you're behind on your rent, and we don't accept T-shirts.

Francis: [nervous laughter] That's quite amusing. But I'm sure the fans sitting at home would like to see my childhood bedroom.

Mother: Oh, I'm sure they would! That sounds like a fantastic idea. Show them where your bed was…the wall you did shadow puppets on and discovered your imagination. All the memories come flooding back. Maybe you shed a tear.

Francis: That would be nice, yes.

Mother: Yeah, then that's a real shame that room's off-limits.

Francis: But I was going to tell everyone about how I could see from my window straight into Ruth Weisman's bedroom and how that was the first time I ever saw a woman naked. And the second time. And the third and fourth and fifth! You don't understand; I held firmly to those images through three marriages.

Mother: You wanna see where our washer and dryer used to be before we sold it to get the CD player?

[commercial break]

[sound of crickets]

[sound of footsteps crunching leaves]

Francis: [whispering] Well, it's just after midnight, and we've returned once again to my boyhood home here at 54 Perennial Lane. After we left, I was thinking of how much time I spent here at night and how I reflected in its silence. And for you folks back home to fully appreciate the environment I grew up in, it's important to see it in all its splendorous shades. Leslie, pick up that crowbar. Stay on me.

[gentle music]

Francis: [whispering] In the summertime, we would catch fireflies out here in the yard. It was all so picturesque. In July, we shot fireworks from Maple Cane Soda bottles. *(to Leslie)* Let's check the front door.

[door opening]

Francis: [whispering] It's unlocked. Shh, keep it down. I can't see where I'm walking. Turn on your light. That's better. Oh, my poor home. Look at this place...Looks like an indoor yard sale. And what is that odor? Listen, nobody throws up, OK? I mean it. What is this, a box of taco shells? God, I bet they're so stale. I mean, look, the box is losing its color. Come on, let's go upstairs.

[footsteps]

Francis: Oh, s***! It's OK; it's just Ethan. Hey, buddy, what are you doing up so late...standing eerily alone in the dark? Couldn't sleep? Here, you want your sponge? OK, he's fine, he's got his sponge, let's keep going.

[stairs creaking]

Francis: Everybody, watch your step, the floor's soft here.

[floorboards squeaking]

Francis: Down the hall...Leslie, gimme the crowbar. I said, "Give me the crowbar," not a look of disapproval. Thank you. [prying padlock] If we're gonna do this special, we're gonna do it right.

[wood splintering]

[door flinging open]

[sound of labored breathing]

Man: Is that you, madame?

Francis: What the f***?!

Man: Morning already?

Francis: There's a guy tied up! There's a guy tied up in my bedroom!

Man: Hey, I'm Al! I'm just up from the city for a few days. Little weekend getaway. Helps me unwind.

[floorboard creaking]

Mother: I said that room's off-limits! *(to Ethan)* Isn't that right, sweetie?

Francis: Oh, s***, run!!

[footsteps running]

Francis: The f***! [heavy breathing] Leslie? Where's Leslie? Leslie?! There's no time...

[footsteps running]

Francis: We tried everything. She's gone. We'll remember her kindness and fashion sense.

[door opening]

[sound of crickets]

Francis: Did you get that? What was that? Who was that guy? There was so much leather. So much.

[sound of stick breaking under footstep]

Mother: I told you people that room was off-limits. *(to Ethan)* Isn't that right—

Francis: S***, get in the car, hurry!

[car doors opening]

[car doors closing]

[car engine struggling to turn over]

[sounds of Mother banging on the windshield]

Francis: You know, this reminds me of those early winter mornings with my old man trying to thaw the engine. I pretended we were stuck on the side of a mountain in a downed plane. He'd yell, "Francis, dammit, get your hands out of your pants."

[engine turning over]

[car speeding off]

[sounds of an old car on a dirt road]

[touching music]

Francis: Well, we're driving to the hotel now. This time in the, uh, in the right direction. It's about three in the morning. Everybody's pretty worn out. Some good and solid sack time is just what the family doctor ordered. And if we get there in six minutes, we'll log us, oh, just under three hours. I remember when all this was farmland. What would you call it now? A lot?

[motel sign buzzing]

Francis: All in all, I think it was a very successful first day. An interesting first day. But I think that's also what one hopes to gain from returning home. Something unexpected. Something surprising. Shocking, actually. In fact, I still can't get a few of the startling images out of my head. I know I'm going to have a difficult time eating cocktail wieners from here on out. But I'm happy to see that New Bridgeburg certainly hasn't lost its small-town charm. May have picked up a little edge, and some, some riffraff with unconventional lifestyles here and there, but that's to be expected. As the country changes, so does New Bridgeburg. And I, for one, am excited to see how the rest of the town's developed over the years. The people...my old school...and, of course, my favorite fishin' hole. I'm predicting some wonderful things. Until then, I'm going to get a little shuteye while you enjoy these commercials brought to you by some really fine people.

[commercial break]

[sound of an old car struggling]

[sounds of a radio scanning stations]

Francis: I won't be shy about telling you folks at home I'm a tad anxious over this next stop. When we get there, you'll know why. However, I'm happy to report that our fearless leader, Leslie, found her way back to the hotel last night and we, we couldn't be more thrilled. Now, it should be up here on the left, right next to the old car wash and the road you take to get out to the trash repository. There it is…Isn't that something? I feel like I've been playing hooky for forty years. Most would say I have been. Let's check it out.

[birds chirping]

Francis: I think I can wholeheartedly say there was never a stage more terrifying than this one behind me—high school. There's nothing unusual or particularly profound about that. It's something we all experience and experience differently. Today, this is the remedial high school. At least that's what they say. We've been here for a solid two hours and haven't seen any kind of a sign with the school's name or any indication of a staff or students. There're cars in the parking lot, and look, here's a candy bar wrapper, so obviously people come here. Before this was a place of education, it was the largest crematorium in the northeast, built by the Wallace-Brewster Stove Company. Before that it was a toaster factory. Also, by Wallace-Brewster. Before the toaster factory, it was a field where they found these large stones in a circular design, and buried in the ground, were human and animal bones. Archeologists believe it was a sacred space used for ritualistic killings, even cannibalism. But during my stay, it was New Bridgeburg High, home of the Swirlin' Oak Leafs. Leslie, here, let's do a yearbook montage with jivey jazz piano.

[erratic jazz music]

[sound of footsteps squeaking]

Francis: There's an old saying out there, which typically finds favor among middle-aged despondency and doomed wedding toasts, about high school being the best years of your life. And I think to some degree, that's true because high school is a time of self-discovery. It's also a time of confusion. A time when we begin to ask the difficult questions, and drastically alter what little we've learned of ourselves up to this point in an unwavering pursuit to get some. This is the main hallway, which we did our best back then to avoid because this is where you have the administrative office. I ran a fairly successful joke writing ring that I had to keep under wraps. I would write jokes for my classmates. You know, stuff to yell out in the middle of a lesson and make everybody cut up. Stuff like...The teacher would ask, "What's the remainder?" And the kid would say, "You alone on a Saturday night." You know, real personal stuff that would cut a body deep. But I grew out of that. And for those that were strapped for cash or without a decent trade, I'd give them some funny-sounding words like "Snuffenpoodle" or "Cluckluck," which simply saying aloud was a popular form of entertainment at the time. At one point, I had a team of three guys and one girl writing for me, which by radio writing standards of the 40s was an equal hiring ratio and everybody was happy. Did you see that?! I thought I saw someone at the other end of the hall. Probably just a reflection.

[basketball bouncing]

Francis: This is the old gymnasium. I was never really into sports, but Leslie here thought it would be nice to get some shots of a man of advancing years struggling to achieve something as simple as making a basket. In this arena, I mostly remember the pep rallies and the pressure to chant our fight song along with my fellow students. Same with church. Something I remember prominently about growing up was constantly being expected to sing. Everybody was singing. Always. I was always in knots about singing. At my grandfather's funeral, my mother, out of the blue, called me up to the pulpit to sing a song, as if I just had something prepared and whatnot. For five minutes, I went through all the corporate radio jingles I could think of…Snappy's Little Grazer Push Mower…which I did in the voice of Snappy the Turtle. I even threw in the pledge of allegiance. And nobody seemed to notice. Afterward, everybody shook my hand and thanked me.

[school desk creaking]

Francis: This was my desk for shorthand with Mr. Beachum. And I mean that literally. This is the actual desk I sat in for shorthand at eight o'clock with Mr. Beachum. If you look right up under the writing surface here, you'll find a sampling of my silver-tongued, adolescent wit. Can you make that out? Can you make out what it says? "This sux." See, I got the "x" in there for sucks, which displays a natural talent for shorthand. It was donated to the town museum a little over ten years ago, where it was auctioned off in 1976 to a Dorothy Lacey of Chautauqua Hollow, New York, 23 East Falls Road. Send her a letter and let her know you heard her name on television. And Miss Lacey was kind enough to lend us the desk in hopes of recreating a little magic from the past. Because standing right out there in the hallway is Mr. Beachum himself. Now, I haven't seen Mr. Beachum since I graduated out of here in 1944. The producers tried to pull one over on me by trying to set up this whole thing as a surprise. And I gotta hand it to them; they did a pretty good job of keeping it from me. So, without further achoo…let's get this little experiment rolling. America, I'd like you to welcome my high school shorthand teacher Mr. Charles Beachum.

[sound of squeaking wheels]

[sound of mechanical pumps]

Francis: Is that—Is that an iron lung? When I found out, you couldn't have mentioned that part? [talking loudly] Good afternoon, Mr. Beachman. You look well-rested. Can he hear me? No, he can't hear me. I gotta say, he looks shorter. I mean it. I know he's lying down, but he looks like an abbreviated version of how I remember him.

[knocking on port windows]

Francis: Can I knock on the window here? Oh, don't knock? [talking loudly] Mr. Beachum? I was hoping we could do some of the old exercises. I think that would be fun for the audience back home.

[loud mechanical sounds]

[sound of frantic writing]

Francis: What's the appropriate symbol for that pump sound? The beeps I got. I just need that inflating sound. Maybe the medium-sized hook? I'm not entirely sure if that's accurate, but I'm having a mental image of a medium-sized hook.

[commercial break]

[sounds of traffic]

Francis: Now that we've completed our lessons for the day, it's only natural that we put down the books and take in this fresh autumn air. I always loved walking down this street because the bakery sat up there on the corner of Kessel. You could smell it good in the mornings: fresh rolls, chocolate layer cake, old-fashioned vanilla. Little did we know at the time that it was a front for the Lombardo crime family. They operated here for a short while in the 30s. It was a kind of pitstop outside the city on route north. Internally, the organization referred to it as "The Sweet Shop." Now, over here, we've got a real treat. This is Norville's Barber Shop. This is where I got my first haircut. Well, my first haircut that wasn't given by my mother. My mother didn't have the best visual perception, so for the first several years of my life, I had extremely uneven bangs. Leslie, no photo. In fact, I developed a wry neck just trying to walk straight. Let's go inside!

[door opening]
[bell chiming]

Francis: Roger? Hi, Roger, it's nice to meet you. I'm Francis.

Roger: Oh, we know all about you.

Francis: Yeah, well, I guess you kind of do, in a way. Suppose everybody does. Now, Norville was your grandfather?

Roger: That's correct.

Francis: Leslie, get a shot of this old ad clipping here on the wall. "Norville's Barber Shop. Norville Coleman, proprietor." And look what it says here…"Four and a half chairs. No waiting." I'd say that's pretty darn good service.

Roger: Dad was a big fan of yours.

Francis: Well, I must tell you, that's a relief. I see a lot of pointy objects around here. You know, it seems you make a few affectionate wisecracks over the years and it feels like the whole town's turned on you.

[sound of scissors]

Roger: Well, you're always welcome here. Let's get you in a chair. Now, what did you want to do today?

Francis: Well, clearly, you haven't surveyed the land too carefully. Trees are a tad thin these days.

Roger: [laughter] Well, we'll see what we can do.

Francis: You're the artist. But seriously, Roger, just a light trim on the sides. I've got a roast next week. Actually, if you could just hold the scissors that'd be great.

Roger: We'll set cha up.

[sound of electric trimmer]

Francis: Heard any good stories lately? I remember when this place was filled, it was quite the sewing circle. I mean, this crew was a catty bunch. And Norville, oh, he was the worst. My father would bring me in when I was younger. I'd sit right over there in the corner. Used to be a leather sofa sat right over there. And, oh, they would gossip and cackle all afternoon. And Norville would always have the juiciest little tidbit. But he never gave up his source. Not once. He was honorable that way, through and through. I heard your father was the same. I never knew him, though. Stanley, right? I was sorry to hear of his passing. He was a grade behind me. Now, I see you're putting foil in my hair...What's that for?

Roger: It helps strengthen the follicles.

Francis: Is that right? Well, it just goes to show you can't stifle ingenuity. How's it look, Leslie? I gotta tell you I can feel it working. It's like a tingling. Well, look at you! A chip off the old Norville block. You know, you wouldn't think of it from the look out front, but you've really, you know, modernized this place. Made it your own. I'm particularly fond of that fern in the corner. I always felt this place could benefit from a bit of softness. I'm sure your father would be proud.

Roger: Do you remember a woman named Lucille Steinkamp?

Francis: Steinkamp? I went to school with a *Lucy* Steinkamp. I haven't thought of Lucy in years, though.

Roger: Do you remember the last time you saw her?

Francis: Oh, wow. I guess that, that would have been back in high school. No, actually, that's not true. I met Lucy in Santa— No, in San Francisco. But that was, that was over twenty, twenty-five years ago.

That was back when I was working The Blue Eye. She was in town visiting. She actually came to see my act. You know Lucy Steinkamp?

Roger: She's my mother.

Francis: No kidding? Well, I'll be. So, Stanley Coleman went and married Lucy Steinkamp. Howdya like that.

Roger: She left New Bridgeburg after dad died.

Francis: Losing someone close is never easy.

Roger: She spoke highly of you, though.

Francis: Lucy was a lovely girl. Her father worked for Connecticut Power if I'm not mistaken. They had an office on Oakwood.

Roger: Hey, look...we both have cleft chins.

Francis: Yeah...yeah, how 'bout that.

[sound of scissors]

Roger: When my mother left San Francisco, did she ever write you?

Francis: I-I don't— [clearing throat] Write? No, I-I don't believe so.

Roger: The reason I ask is because after dad died, I found a box of letters addressed to you.

Francis: So, you ever do any of those perms? Are they still in?

Roger: Seems she wrote to you over a dozen times telling you she was pregnant.

Francis: I, uh— That's, uh— Pregnant?

Roger: In one of them, she mentioned trying to reach you at the club. She got some guy but could hear you in the background say, "Hang up the phone, it's that girl I knocked up."

Francis: [nervous laughter] Huh, howdya— Well, you know— Joke— I'm a joker— Jokester. W-W-Why do you ask?

Roger: I was just curious.

[sound of electric trimmer]

[sounds of traffic]

Francis: Yeah, I, uh— Give me a moment. Listen, this, this isn't working. We have to stop doing these things where we go and talk to people. Seriously, each one is more traumatic than the last. I don't think I can take much more. I mean, don't you f****** people research? What the s*** does my staff even do all day?! You go in for a haircut and to exchange a few innocent yarns from your past and you walk out with a f****** kid. F***!

[sigh]

Francis: He what? He put highlights in my hair? Highlights? B-B-Bring the camera in...Oh my god, I look like a South Beach nightclub owner. That little jerk. I'm sure he picked up that one from his mother. What? What do you mean there's something shaved into the back of my head? Well, what is it? A dollar sign?! Oh my god, I can feel it. Well, this is great. Just great! Alright, no more people. We need to get away from the people, get out of town— We need to get as far away from town as possible. No good is coming from town! F****** Lucy f****** Steinkamp.

[sigh]

Francis: OK, let's run through this...Well, how do I look? I think he did a pretty good job!

[sound of an old car on a back road]

Francis: No trip to New Bridgeburg would be quite complete without a leisurely afternoon drive through the countryside with nobody else around. Like the ones my family and I used to take after church on Sundays. An opportunity to marvel at New England's vibrant autumn colors. Photographer Shamus Browning once wrote: "The Native Americans have a saying...'The shadows are longest before they disappear.'" Doesn't have anything to do with Connecticut. In fact, he was high on peyote when he said it.

[car rattling over bumps]

Francis: There was a restaurant up the road a ways called The Old Watermill Restaurant. To get to go was always a treat for us. One time, my old man accused the waitress of stealing the gristle off his filet. I have this image of the chef yelling at my father, trying to convince him that the filet is a lean cut. My father was adamant, even though he didn't know what he was talking about. That's just the kind of man he was. He threw a baked potato against the wall and called the chef a "meat fondler." Whatever that meant. I remember, at one point, a woman from another table putting her hand on my shoulder. That always stuck with me for some reason. Driving up there, we would make sure to cross over the old McIntyre covered bridge up here. Isn't that something else? Now, have you ever seen a more picturesque bridge in all your life? With the trees here...just marvelous. A well-known painter by the name of Bob Roland once did a painting of it but lost it before anyone could see it. The bridge was named for Samuel McIntyre, one of the founders of New Bridgeburg. He left town shortly after it was established to pursue a bizarre crusade aimed at straightening all the county's rivers. He was an efficient man and felt that most rivers could be more direct than they were. Apparently, he was pretty outspoken on the matter. Almost to an annoying degree. So, everybody was happy when he left town. Still, it remains a proud and cherished symbol of New Bridgeburg.

[faint sounds of a stream]

[moving piano music]

Francis: This is probably one of my favorite spots in all of New Bridgeburg. This is the Bartoll River, and it flows down from those mountains behind me in the distance. My father would bring me here Saturday mornings to go fishing. Sometimes we would fish all day. We never really caught all that much. Oh, I'm sure there was the occasional landing of a big one. But it was never about the fishing. It was about the peacefulness and sharing something with my father. Although, it didn't take many trips for me to realize that in his eyes, my sole purpose was to hand him things he could easily reach himself. Our conversations were limited to single words, which usually suggested the thing he wanted me to hand him. He said he was teaching me, but honestly, I felt more like an undervalued assistant...or an end table. Still, it was the gentle placidity of the area I found so comforting. Listen to that...The calm of the water and its trickling steadfast tranquility. There's a beautifully unbiased essence to nature. Similar to childlike wonderment, which continues to resonate in the youthful spirit of this aging man, still empowered by the impossible. I think we're all guilty of taking it for granted as we live our busy—

[faint sounds of machinery]

[faint sounds of activity in the water]

Sheriff: OK, boys, nice and easy now...

Francis: Ah, look...Fellow anglers. Is that the sheriff? Howdya like that, town's so sleepy even the law has time to sit back and cast a line.

Sheriff: OK, boys, set 'im down here...

Francis: Looks like they, uh— Yeah, looks like they caught 'em a big one. Oh my god. Is that, is that a body? Son of a—

Sheriff: [shouting] Let's fire up the crane.

[sound of a crane]

Sheriff: OK, boys, hoist her on out of there...

Francis: Look! They're pulling something from the river. What the- What is that? Is that a car? No, no...It's a plane!

Sheriff: Steady now...

Francis: Leslie, follow me...

Sheriff: Alright, boys, open her up.

[metal prying open]

[water spilling]

Francis: Leslie, what, what are those bushels wrapped up? Is that— Are those drugs?! Of course, they're drugs.

Sheriff: Today's catch of the day, boys—a hundred kilos of Columbian pixie dust.

[faint sound of trucks approaching from a distance]

Francis: Huh...Must be the local news.

[sounds of machine-gun fire]

Sheriff: Take cover; it's the cartel!

Francis: S***! Get down! They've come for the drugs!

[sounds of police officers being shot]

Francis: Oh my god, it's the hair! They think I'm a rival trafficker!

[indiscernible shouting in Spanish]

Francis: [shouting] They're just highlights! From my illegitimate son for abandoning his mother! They're revenge highlights!

[gunfire ceasing]

[faint sound of Sheriff pleading]

Francis: [whispering] Nobody make a sound...I think they're talking to the sheriff.

[gunshot]

Francis: Yeah, they shot him. The sheriff's dead. They're all dead. OK, time to go! Everybody, get in the f****** car! Leslie, get the f*** in the car!

[indiscernible shouting in Spanish]

[sounds of gunfire]

[sound of engine struggling to turn over]

[sound of car starting]

Francis: Go, go, go, go!!! Get the f*** to the airport!!

[sound of a plane taking off]

[touching string music]

Flight Attendant: Another martini, Mr. O'Donnell?

Francis: Yeah...Just park the cart behind me, would cha.

Flight Attendant: Mr. O'Donnell, are you OK? You appear to be bleeding.

Francis: It's, uh…it's not my blood.

[sound of drinking]

Francis: Well, there you have it, folks…my hometown…and all its, its magnificence. The people and places and events that were so instrumental in my formative years. I'm reminded of the old maxim of small-town values: "Hard work, determination, and a sense of community." The fundamental ingredients in a well-balanced upbringing. I'm also thinking of a few other choice words, like cesspool and witness protection. Can I get a hot towel over here?! A famous poet with a recognizable name once said, "A person's home follows them wherever they go. Like a fully furnished trailer." I'm not entirely sure what that means. In fact, now that I think about it, I believe I got that off a promotional pamphlet or something. Who knows? But, looking back on it all, my memories of home remain the fondest I own. And the most disturbing. Just utterly terrifying.

[glass bottles clinking]

Francis: [toasting] Here's to going back.

Flight Attendant: [intercom] The captain has turned on the fasten seatbelt sign.

[music swells]

TGIBF

*B*lood of Christ? Blood of Christ? Care for a free sample? Ah, I thought I had that guy. Where is everybody? It's Black Friday; the mall should be packed. Look around; it's dead. Ugh, I don't know, ya know? Things used to be different. This day used to mean something to people. *Blood of Christ? Blood of Christ?* It's like people have forgotten the true meaning of Black Friday. Everybody does all their shopping online these days. And they've made it into something it isn't—a digital freakshow. One-click sacraments and on-demand salvation. People don't remember the fun of a brick-and-mortar communion shop. *Free sample? Free sample? Sir? He that eateth my flesh hath everlasting life—* Aah! See what I mean? Probably has boxes of wafers waiting for him at home. Where's the enjoyment? The spirit? The thrill of waiting in line for hours on end for the newest chalice? Bundled up in your favorite folding chair with a thermos of pumpkin spice lattes or the season's first peppermint. David in the stock room said that some coffee places started serving peppermint drinks weeks ago. Is nothing sacred?!

And yes, what about pumpkin spice? Let's talk pumpkin spice. Can we please talk about this war on pumpkin spice?! Where has it been? It used to be everywhere. And now there're all these other flavors showing up that no one's even heard of before. Praline...Brûlée...Tell me, what the heck is brûlée? These days you're lucky to get a pumpkin toaster pastry.

I hate to be the first to say it, but things have changed. What happened to the joy of the hunt? Racing down the aisle to snag that last complete communion set in silver. Frantically rifling through bins of wheat wafers looking for white. Jews and gentiles alike wrestling the remaining box of unsalted matzo bread from each other's grips. How did Black Friday get so mixed up and muddled? Have we completely done away with tradition? What happened to that magical month on the calendar where we pulled ourselves up out of the red and jumped into the black? The tentpole—revival—that kept us afloat all year. The unification of merchants in a festive celebration of economic exchange. A rejoiceful and jubilant, money-making observance of faith-based goods and services. A day without a competitive market. That collective cash-in that brought us all closer together. Where are those days? *Free sample?* Scattered throughout the macrocosm of the Interweb, that's where. How are we supposed to contend with free two-day shipping? Tell me? *Sir, free sample? Sir? All brass-tone bread plates, sixty percent off! Ma'am?*

I don't even know why we bother anymore. Nobody's listening. Just trying to kill some time before their movie—*So-And-So's Big Holiday*. And every year it's the same. It's becoming the norm. As long as they can get the Eucharist online, they don't need to go to the store. Shoppers these days…they're so spoiled. I mean, everywhere you look, it's religious convenience. Blessed offerings beamed right into their palms with the tap of a screen. "Oh, I want to; it's just easier to observe from home," they say. You know, I'm starting to think this whole concept is just a thing of the past…Black Friday. Oh, sure, some of them will show up for returns…gift cards…you know? When they need us. When they read those three little words: "Out of stock." It's just not the same, you know. Slogging in shopping bags of sanctity with corneas stained red from taillights. Soaking wet with Autumn rain. That sense of accomplishment and pride coursing through your body like the holy spirit because you grabbed the deal of the day! The smell of gingerbread wafting from the food court. The joyous sounds of holiday cheer reverberating along the indoor promenade. The sanctimonious clank of copper communionware and hearts filled with mirth. I just don't get it! What did we do wrong?! Did we not exhibit grace in the face of progress and an acceptance of new ideas and methods of commerce? Were we not open…late enough? Were we asking too much…of them? I mean, it's just one day!

I tell ya, I weep for the fellowship of this country and the future of communion retail. What are we gonna do with all this grape juice? Drink it? I'll pretend I didn't hear that. You know, Michael heard that most of the online stores started Black Friday sales last week. Can you believe that? Some as early as the 31st. October! What's the point anymore? Might as well just close up shop for all of April while we're at it! Doesn't appear it would make any difference! I mean, have you ever? Ha, they've got a prayer! Oh, who am I kidding? They're over there rollin' in it. Wherever there is!

Face it, my friend, we're yesterday's news. There's just too many other options out there today. That's the problem. The market's overrun. Flashy alternatives with pseudo payment options. Stores without nearly the same standing or shelf life. How are people to know if they're making the right bet? They don't. And do they care? No. They jump in the first basket to come floatin' down the river. *Half off prefilled communion cups, five hundred count? Care for a sample?* It's probably a regional thing. You know, where you live. See, the rural areas still like a good building. And a parking lot. Big signs and a greeter. They want that one-on-one experience. Everything in one place, you know. While in the cities, it's just a free-for-all. Phone apps and robot lockers. As long as it's different. That's all they care about. They'll open their doors to just any ole body. And I'll tell you this…I guarantee you those folks coming in aren't drinkin' pumpkin spice.

God bless the megastore, am I right? Keeping this whole thing alive. *Free sample? Sir? Celebration, fellowship, remembrance? Plenty of cases left! Ma'am? Ma'am? This is my body…This is my body!* My friend Bartholomew said that with all the malls and stores closing around him, you can't even find a decent communion. Let alone supplies. It's sad. Oh, but they're shoutin' praises online. Bunch o' bells and whistles, if ya ask me. And you know how it happens, don't you?

One year you get bogged down with work, the kids, and through blind desperation, you stray from the herd. "Oh, it was just that one time, I promise." The following year rolls around— *Blood of Christ? Blood of Christ? Half off all absolutions*— The following year rolls around, and you find yourself in a similar predicament. But by then, it's too late. Last year's transgression has all but moved in for the season and planted a personalized holiday photo on your mantel, with a tacky sweater and blurred edges for softness. And where do you think they had that photo printed? Hm? When was the last time you saw Fran's Photo Kiosk without the tarp? Hmmm? And not to mention some weird dish your new digitally ingrained holiday guest insists on cooking at all hours of the night. The kind that lingers for days in the fibers of your clothing. Campfires of competing intensities you need professional work to drive out. I'm tellin' you, you, it's a sorry state of affairs we're living in. *Free sample? Free sample? Your one-stop shop for forgiveness! Envy, lust, greed, seventy-five percent off! Sir?* I mean, you get what I'm sayin'. *Ma'am? We got great deals on wrath. Discount salvation, right this way!* Yeah, you're a smart kid, you know what I'm sayin'.

Look at these people…Remnants of holiday shopping past. Ghosts of a commercial triumph. Wandering aimlessly, if not for some sick form of kitsch. "Let's all go to the mall ironically." Indifferent to the woes of mom and pop. While a sad handful of them remain true, trapped in a loop and wrapped in chains forged by a cyber monopoly. *Ma'am? Ma'am? After the supper, he took the cup.* Platinum online shopper, I bet you anything. Probably has a stockpile of points. *Sir?*

Sir? I know you can hear me. That's the same as lying— What you're doing is the same as lying! Stop in for a quick sacrament? Absolve your sins? Phew. That hits the spot.

Uh-oh...we're out of gluten-free bread. No, these are from the back! No, nothing's open! What are we going to do? Without a gluten-free option, we don't stand a chance of turning a profit this season. Online? Nah, nah, nah, I-I-I don't think so. Did you not just hear me?! What's the matter with you, bringing that up? Listen, I know I said some crazy things back there, but we're brick-and-mortar loyalists. It's the principle. Yeah, well, I don't see any water crackers around here, do you? "Water crackers." Look, if we don't get some gluten-free sacraments stat, that's it. Do you hear me? It's over. They win. Yeah, well, I don't care if they're here to stay. Yes, yes, I realize these are desperate times. Survival, huh? I suppose the ends do justify the means. I have heard that. And this is an emergency. M-Maybe I'll just see how much they are. Couldn't hurt, right? Yeah. Oh...Uh, whaddya know. I already ordered them. They'll be here within the hour. Well, that was convenient.

Listen...I been doing some thinking the last ten seconds, and...maybe, maybe we were a bit too quick to judge. Perhaps we're going about this whole thing the wrong way. Maybe the answer isn't one or the other, but a balance of the two. What if there were good in both? And bad in both? What if we could enjoy the convenience of modern commerce while still having an appreciation for traditional trade and customs? That way, there's not such a hard divide between the people that want change and the people that liked things the way they were. We're never going to convince one another to switch sides. And that's OK. But perhaps together, we could find some common ground. A place from where we can share with one another new practices in an ever-diversifying culture and market. Weed out the bad in both and promote the good. Together. And in the process, gain a better understanding of what it really is each side believes. You know, and what they want in their shopping experience. Instead of basing our opinions on ratcheted-up, outdated rhetoric. And yes, together, redefine the entire season in contemporary terms. And, along the way, hopefully, rediscover the true meaning of Black Friday—the monetization of the holidays and making as much money as possible.

We should probably sell something else, though, because this religion junk is really drivin' a wedge between us all and getting in the way of everybody's good time.

Written in the Stars

*I*f winter is the season to be merry and summer is the season for love, when is the season for misery? When is the season for sorrow? Or the season for heartbreak? A recent study from Brown University suggests somewhere around the third week in September. So, mark your calendars, you unlucky ones. Of course, there really is no optimal time to have your emotional entrails strung out in the immediate wake of a breakup or the parking lot of a casual dining restaurant—particularly one surrounded by so many nail salons and hobby shops and consisting primarily of vehicles with dually wheels and opinionated back-windows; as well as tow hitches with genitalia. But how did things get to this low point? Was it a question of chemistry? It certainly couldn't have been algebra. Or was it a problem with shared interests? Religion? Children? Was there no love? But what is love? I tell you what, answer that one, and you've got a million-dollar idea. Don't answer it, and you'll have an idea roughly worth the income of a single, sad, and lonely person.

People fall in and out of love daily. Sometimes twice a day. You know, if it's particularly sunny out, and you want to make the most of it. But why does love sometimes fail? That is, the chemical reaction we perceive as love—the rearrangement of molecules and ions that cause us to view five years in an animal- and mold-filled studio apartment with a practical stranger and an unidentified drip through rose-colored glasses. Why is it not the constant we, car commercials, and investment groups make it out to be? What's the key to a long-running and truly happy relationship? To answer these questions (and a whole lot less), we needn't look further than the stars.

Millions of people put a great deal of stock in astrology. Some of whom are surprisingly coherent. It's true. Why, even most skeptics have a hard time ignoring an accurate horoscope or the chest of your friend's roommate that's into tarot. Call it coincidence or generalizations that apply to the human condition, or the aforementioned horniness, there's something to be said for the public's interest in celestial divination and its uncanny accuracy. For thousands of years, whether forecasting the future or the weather, humans have gathered insight into their lives and lifestyles through the observation of astronomical bodies in the sky and their orbital revolution and rotation. Which is like a tiny little spinning party within a party—that exclusive booth in the corner of the club that's the envy of every Instagrammer. The stars and planets and their moons, and their relative positions, have paved the planetary way for a myriad of predicting practices. Most notably, the calendrical system and horoscopic astrology—a visual representation pertaining to the angles of said revolving bodies and the birth of an individual.

By now, you've probably figured out where I'm going with all this. In that case, go on ahead of me and let my dog out; I wanna peruse the picture books. That's right, folks, the Zodiac—an area of the sky where specifically the position and path of the sun and moon and other pedestrian planetary bodies are charted over the course of a calendar year, with a recognized two-week vacation and five sick days, which unfortunately don't roll over. The Zodiac is divided into twelve signs (the Nina, the Pinta, and the Santa Maria repeated four times), each consisting of thirty degrees of celestial longitude, ranging from 0 to 360, with the first astrological sign, Aries, starting at degree 0 and marking the vernal equinox. Each sign also contains a meaning and symbol, an element, a ruling planet, color, day of the week, flower, and a bunch of other stuff that's just impossible to make funny. And, most importantly, now that the crash course is out of the way, the entire reason we've gathered here in the first place—a sign's compatibility with another sign. Love on a cosmic level. So, in the interest of word count and wasting valuable Tender time, we'll forego listing all the signs now and, instead, dive right in.

As I mentioned a moment ago, in case you missed it, courtesy of the Columbus-multiplication bit, the Zodiac that we've all come to know and love—mainly out of dating survival—begins as the sun shines brightly through the constellation Aries. Born in the span of March 21st and April 19th, Aries is a natural-born leader, which will certainly clear up confusion on the dance floor, as well as in the bedroom. That is, if you don't mind a frank and controlling lover that may refer you to a PowerPoint on positions, which they created in the five minutes between back-to-back meetings and volunteering to head yet another project they themselves brought to the attention of the team—a team of which they're surely the director. Aries is most compatible with Leo. With the same ruling planet of Mars and the same element of fire, Aries and Leo are a red-hot match that will have a hard time sitting still. Unless they're involved in a particularly adventurous sex act consisting of a bullwhip and the balancing of wooden chairs end-on-end, which will undoubtedly call for absolute steadiness. Leo, the lion, will call this act "the three-ring cunnilingus." You'll get there or die trying. Their forthright language, stick-to-itiveness—though sometimes resulting in a flare-up of TMJ—and aversion to idleness, is the glue that binds Aries and Leo. Unfortunately, their unending fun paraded on social media will sicken most other couples, especially those who have been talking about having a baby for the past eight years. Furthermore, singles scrolling well into the night—a night that most likely ended around 6 p.m.—will be hit the hardest, as they unconvincingly claim that the constant display of recreation and amusement had by Aries and Leo looks as exhausting as their perky faces and stupid smiles.

Next in line is Taurus, meaning the bull, whose symbol looks like the obvious circle with horns, or a promise ring tied to the bottom portion of a black, artificial leather necklace worn by an 8th grader dressed almost entirely in jersey. Even more sickening than the show put on by Aries and Leo, the observed love between Taurus and their most compatible sign, Cancer, will undoubtedly cause a complete boycott of romantic comedies by single folks, if not a bonfire of DVDs on one's front lawn. That is, of course, if Taurus and Cancer's soul-crushing, soulmate bond hasn't already sent the, in all likelihood, unlovable, into an arms-flailing, hate-filled downward spiral ending in drawn blinds, piling take-out containers, and extended periods of cheek-to-carpet contact. Empirical and typically a homebody, with a birthday falling between April 20th and May 20th, Taurus is stable yet stubborn and calls to mind an image of someone tirelessly pushing on a large, immovable cow. Like Taurus, Cancer is loyal and family-oriented and prefers planting themselves at home rather than going out to socialize; say, at a three-day music festival with ragweed and an unsettling toilet-to-attendee ratio. Not to mention Cancer's likely reluctance to shell out four hundred bucks for the experience, which speaks to their frugalness and quite possibly their overall sense. Though I can't say for sure; I haven't seen the lineup. These homey and nurturing characteristics support both signs in their innate pursuit to create a cute little world of their own. A world comprised of love and sentimentality with the questionably healthy hoarding of not just pictures but every baby tooth, toenail clipping, macaroni craft, love note, police citation, and frozen poppy petal from their days of courting that surely fill their freezer.

Continuing along the ecliptic, extending through the 60th degree, is Gemini. A conversationalist at heart and an admirer of words and the romance of language, Gemini is a talker; but a restrained one compared to some of the more extroverted signs. Thankfully for those into dirty talk, this chatty trait of Gemini can turn sultry in a heartbeat—or a skipped heartbeat, for that matter—and will surely carry weight in the bedroom, if not before, say with a saucy text in the company of family or a suggestive Scrabble play, also in the company of family. Preferably a word with a 'J' or a 'Z' and landing on a triple tile, as Gemini also exhibits a mildly competitive spirit, which too carries weight in the bedroom. The best sign to pair with this intellectual and enlightening trip is the similarly bright Libra. Hours will fall off the clock when these two engage in stimulating conversation, which may include a range of fascinating topics from phyllotactic spirals in native southwestern flora and spiritual metaphysics as it applies to inner awareness to late-nineteenth-century studies in linguistics and intelligent breakfast cereals. The only thing to drive a wedge between these two is their indecisiveness and Gemini's possible curiosity regarding said indecisiveness, which together they'll expound on for several hours, or until Libra loses interest and tries to order a pizza from the same slice shop that's been closed for four years.

Next up is our first water sign, the complex and seemingly temperamental, especially when confronted with a tasteless 'Yo Mama' joke—unless it's particularly creative—Cancer. From our brief examination of Taurus, we know Cancer is home-based in nature and finds fulfillment in helping others, specifically loved ones. That is unless said loved ones test their loyalty. In which case, Cancer's Moon ruler will cause a werewolf-like transformation that will surely make the Hulk look like a kiwi fruit globule; an adorable analogy if you imagine a kiwi's cute little hairy skin. Moreover, in pursuit of varying cosmic couples and the excuse to continue my exhibition of dense prose—which is the literary equivalent of an action film with a bunch of quick cuts and a storyline that fizzles out after the sex scene—Cancer can also enjoy a lovely night in with Virgo; that is, if Taurus doesn't find out. If that happens, then you can kiss those finger paintings on the fridge goodbye. Cancer and Virgo thrive in their ability to communicate; this is their foundation, and when mixed with Virgo's awareness of Cancer's volatile tendencies and understanding of one another's emotional needs, it's nothing short of pure harmony. Unless Virgo can't take Cancer's "Yes" for an answer and becomes overly sensitive and smothers Cancer with insistent Are-you-OK's over and over, then the whole melody's gonna sound like crap. And don't expect for a second that sex with Cancer is mechanical or passionless, given their seemingly reserved surface. Sex with Cancer isn't sex at all, but more lovemaking, and is such a powerful and emotionally intense experience, Virgo would be well-advised to bring an extra box of tissues. That is, for the tears, of course.

The fifth astrological sign in the chart, with a birthday between July 23rd and August 22nd, is the fixed sign of Leo, which refers to the sign's quality and not their inability to procreate—a mix-up that caused quite the bother within the late-eighteenth-century American dating scene. Contrary to colonial error, Leo, as mentioned earlier, is all about imagination and death-defying feats in the bedroom. In addition, they're experts in the art of making love to themselves in the mirror, specifically the big one hanging over their bed. Besides Aries, Leo will also find a lively, hip-swinging potential soulmate in Sagittarius—which sounds like a kind of jailbait for dinosaurs. These two are an impulsive and frisky pair that wins the astrological award for most likely to quit their jobs in an over-the-top fashion, spending the entirety of their savings on a soul-searching, relationship-strengthening road trip through Central and South America. Only to find themselves penniless and five days without a shower, bedding down behind a Costa Rican car rental service in the back of a panel-less '84 Volvo sitting on cinder blocks, after being conned by a fellow, hard-partying, carefree couple named Ravi and Zanna. Sagittarius will surely take this opportunity to speak their mind and possibly blame Leo, not just for their current predicament but for the trip altogether. This high may very well fuel a full-blown rant of honesty from Sagittarius that will bounce right off Leo. That is everything but the criticisms from the bedroom, particularly Leo's poor giving-to-taking ratio and their obnoxious glances over Sagittarius's shoulder to get a better look at themselves in the mirror.

Surpassing the 150th degree, rounding out the front stretch and Turns 1 and 2, is Virgo, the Zodiac's stickler for perfection and efficiency, which they'll continually claim is to benefit others. A reasonable and relatively accurate explanation until they freeze in horror after you misuse a semicolon or develop a facial tic watching you cut peppers. Known as the virgin maiden with an affection for wheat, due to their presumed purity, love doesn't come easy for

Virgo—unless there's a beach house in the mix or a zucchini in the trousers. In which case, it comes twice a day and *three* times on Sunday; or not at all if they've had too much to drink or find themselves distracted by the painful remembrance of a past lover or experience an inability to concentrate due to the sidewalk commotion of two drunken tech bros in an unspecified competition to see who can sing Smash Mouth the loudest. Their dating pitfalls are mainly attributed to their perceived pickiness or reluctance to bend. That said, compromise is crucial for Virgo. And the sign most willing to put up with Virgo's love in the form of micromanagement is the optimistic Sagittarius, fresh off the cargo ship from their South American disaster. At first glance, Sagittarius's spontaneity and want for fun may, more often than not, conflict with Virgo's prearranged work schedule. But together, their openness and the previously mentioned willingness to find a middle ground, or at least an enticing trade— preferably one involving oils and a saddle—will take Virgo and Sagittarius far. Luckily, with the perpetual desire and quest for entertainment exhibited by Sagittarius, the mild-mannered, almost shy Virgo delivers a sexual appetite that's just impossible to satisfy— an appetite suited for a sort of erotic all-you-can-eat buffet. That is, a fully stocked erotic buffet and not one, say, moments after the high school across the street lets out.

Next up, just in time for the fall equinox and everything pumpkin, is the cardinal sign of Libra, the walking personification of balance; that is unless there's a fanny pack at play. Specifically, one casually off to the side, as opposed to the formal black, straight on. With a scale as their symbol, there's no denying Libra's capacity for harmony and justice. Libra excels in social skills and loves to question everything, which couples beautifully with the unorthodox thinker, Aquarius. These two are another one of those fun-loving, happy-go-lucky matches that's sure to incite jealousy and long-term obesity (with the aid of alcohol and excess carbs) among single people—aka people that won't let their waiter clear the second place setting because their friend is just stuck in traffic and will be along any minute. Additionally, Libra and Aquarius both want nothing short of the relationship trifecta—a partner, a lover, and a best friend. That is, one standing on two legs, not four. Insert doggy-style pun. Insert "insert" pun. This relationship checklist and playful language display not only the idealistic tendencies of Libra and Aquarius but also their lighthearted sex life, which contains an A-to-Z list of acts and positions that are undoubtedly performed with an accompaniment of giggles and persistent snorts. Role-playing is big with these two, especially the dress-up part, and can sometimes overshadow the actual sex—hoop skirts and bloomers, fishnets and leather—not to mention a host of fun outfits for women. However, problems within this union may occur if Libra becomes too overbearing and simply can't chill the F* out. At which point, space is the best thing for both signs; that or a cute little lace number with bows and a sensible stiletto.

Spanning the 210th to 240th degrees of the Zodiac is the eighth astrological sign, Scorpio. From the constellation Scorpius—the name given to the giant scorpion sent by the Greek deity Gaia to kill Orion, even though most scholars believe Orion was killed by accident when he got his head stuck in his bow and slipped on the constellation Creamy Peanut Butter—Scorpio lives in a black and white world of extremes that sometimes tilts in the direction of the playfully nefarious. Something either is or isn't with Scorpio, and there's rarely a state of in-between. These traits, mixed with a memory that would show up an elephant with a tape recorder, make Scorpio a mysterious force to be reckoned with and clearly one not to be crossed. And who better to be a loyal and emotionally supportive companion with a proclivity for vengefulness than Cancer. Trust is the key in this relationship—trust and separate bedrooms, or at the very least, headphones. Although, Scorpio and Cancer would be wise to supply those separate bedrooms with a joining door, as this is a couple brimming with lust. Their fiery fervor and deep emotion are a display that comfortably rivals the energetic prowess of a ten-year-old boy home alone with a couch cushion. This couple makes mating rabbits look like frayed house slippers lying on top of each other. Sadly though, with pent-up passion courtesy of conflicting schedules or the results of their shared love for chili and corn chips, the romance between Scorpio and Cancer can, over time, begin to exhibit ups and downs similar to an EKG of a geriatric in an orgy of supermodels.

Continuing our exploration of love in the cosmos and book sales for the lonely, a sign we're quite familiar with, by now, the sun transits the constellation Sagittarius between November 22nd and December 21st. Known as the centaur archer, with a bow and arrow symbol that looks like some unknown gender I'd like to spend a long weekend with, Sagittarius is spontaneous and probably chose the spiral in that "Which of these five symbols do you find most pleasing?" test first-year psych majors whip out at parties after everyone is good and tipsy and sitting in a circle in the kitchen. Sagittarius pairs well with most active and intrepid signs, but it's Aries that has the stamina most suited for Sagittarius and their impulsiveness. Which could very easily take on the form of a 1600-mile, two-day drive to the Grand Canyon with a five-hour Navajo weaving workshop sprung on the spur-of-the-moment. Or a late-night impromptu skinny-dipping session in a Roman fountain after cleaning out the liquor cabinet of their Airbnb host; even though they bought a bottle as a thank you but ended up drinking it after they were released by the polizia. Sagittarius and Aries serve as a guiding light for one another, offering an unending source of peerless inspiration and child-like curiosity, which will become quite evident in the midst of that weaving workshop. That is, if it doesn't turn competitive—a characteristic both these signs possess. Thankfully though, both fire signs, Sagittarius and Aries will find a love affair that sizzles like teppanyaki and has more unexpected changes in direction than a local cab driver shuttling tourists.

The tenth sign in our study, with a birthday landing between December 22nd and January 19th, is Capricorn. A sign belonging to the earth element—an element connected to introversion, like water—Capricorn is ruled by Saturn, which is associated with focus and awareness. This speaks a great deal to Capricorn's logic and practicality. A far cry from the sign's symbol, the sea-goat—the most confused and uninspired creature in all of mythology. Like some half evolved prehistoric sea bass that wandered out of the water, saw grassy hills, and went goat. Capricorn favors structure, organization, and, above all, planning—all traits linked to a particular way of life that only another Capricorn could endure. That's right! It's sea-goat on sea-goat action! On their own, these cosmic sweethearts are tough to interpret and take a great deal of time before they're comfortable opening up. This understanding of one another's reticent essence makes Capricorn and Capricorn a perfect match, able to go at their own pace or until their hips cramp up. And though passionate in the bedroom, after reaching speed, so to speak, the proverbial 0 to 60, however, is achieved in a leisurely, sometimes swerving fashion. So, it's safe to say you'll unlikely find a supermarket romance paperback with a cover showing off a gorgeous chested, golden-haired he-man dripping with sweat and sexuality entitled *The Capricorn Seduction*. But where they lack in coordination and aim, they make up for in undying devotion—unless their partner is persistently late and never with a good excuse.

Between January 20th and February 18th, the sun enters the Zodiac's oldest constellation, Aquarius. Known in Latin as the water carrier, this intelligent and inventive sign considers the brain the sexiest organ—but not necessarily the most fun. A libertarian at heart, but · with a regard for serving sizes, Aquarius is the forward-thinker of the Zodiac, an innovator and nonconformist. And not the ostentatious kind that's likely to avoid hallways or leave a room through the window, or, for that matter, use the phrase "I'm a nonconformist." For

Thaddeus Ellenburg's Casual Friday: The Casuals (Volume One)

Aquarius to fall head-over-heels-or-loafers in love, they need a like-minded, equally inquisitive, and broad-minded sign with a tolerance for molly. This honor goes to the colorful and similarly unflappable in the face of the universe's unending kicks to the groining, Gemini. We remember Gemini from earlier as the one with the filthy mouth and spiritual aspirations. This pair is perfect for each other in almost every way. Two brilliant minds spending their days explicating the existential correlation between mind, body, and soul; and doing so through clever and explicit language. And I mean, like, really vulgar stuff. Super hardcore. And though this wondrous duo may need the occasional break from one another, as well as a good reality check and possibly a physical, they'll be eager to return to each other when they realize that no one else can match their enthusiasm for both the beautiful and the ugly sides of the human condition. That said, what others would categorize as ugly, life's terrible and painful experiences—not unlike watching a Shriners parade from start to finish—Aquarius and Gemini would call beautiful and go so far as to label growth. And where their shared willingness to accept new ideas gets really fun is in, of course, the bedroom. Together the nightstands of these two will undoubtedly be holding a medley of lubricants, pleasure toys, and a fifty pack of double-As. Neighbors of Aquarius and Gemini will think this couple is constantly on the electric toothbrush. So, it goes without saying, for Aquarius men and women and Gemini men and women, don't assume who will use what on who and where—everything is fair game with this permissive pair.

226

And last, but certainly not least, mainly due to the fact that this is your author's sign, while at the same time quite possibly serving as the principal reason for its lack of mention until now—a statement that truly represents this sign's unwavering love-hate relationship with itself—Pisces. With a constantly disappointing birthday between February 19th and March 20th, Pisces is the delicate, emotional—though they prefer the word passionate—butterfly of the Zodiac. Pisces is a dreamer, consumed by inspiration, creativity, and woolgathering, as well as a couple of other archaic terms. With a susceptibility to mood swings, it's only natural that Scorpio would calm the unease of the fanciful Pisces. And do so after coming into view unexpectedly over the horizon, backdropped by a brilliantly pristine sky and maybe a UFO. Pisces and Scorpio are another one of those rare, magical twosomes that strike envy among the superficially bonded and, therefore, non-celestial matched couples. With heads and hearts finely tuned for escapism and constant displays of repulsive vulnerability, this pair connects on the deepest levels and is enamored by each party's almost supernatural insight into their partner. Individually, Pisces and Scorpio may easily be the most unusual people you know. Like your sister's high school boyfriend who wore a poncho every day of summer break and was always asking you for a glass of tepid tap water from the basement's unfinished bathroom. But together, in each other's eyes, they're the only other normal person on the planet. Pisces and Scorpio are joined by the unconventional, and value no end their partner's intensity and secret desire for despondency. Between the sheets, these two put on a sensual and zealous display that has all the hallmarks of a tender, tremor-filled Nicholas Sparks love scene. Or, more appropriately, the true and steadfast love between a chubby man and a basket of hot wings.

And so there you have it. The constellations have spoken, wedding bells have rung, and boots have been knocked—twelve perfect couples, written in the stars and destined to live happily ever after. Unless their work spouse turns out to be so much more down-to-earth.

Small Screen Matinee

*G*ood afternoon, everybody. Welcome to Stewart Classic Films; I'm Trevor Laughton. Coming up next on our month-long salute to screen legend Barbara Ritter, we have what most consider the greatest romantic psychological drama ever produced and one of my personal favorites. From Cowen Pictures in 1954, directed by Otto Slazenger, it's *The Ghosts of Wetherby Manor*. Produced by Roy B. Dandridge and based on the 1940 Dorothy Addison novel bearing the same name, Ritter plays a New York fashion journalist sent to Maine on assignment to cover a reclusive French designer at his seaside mansion—played by silent film veteran Jack Humphrey, in what would be his final role alive. In 1977, Humphrey's corpse appeared in the low-budget, independent science fiction/horror film *They Walk Again*, shot on the actor's native Irish soil after the filmmakers stole his body from its tomb in Bel Eaton Derry.

Ritter's character is quickly taken by the charismatic dressmaker, and while questioning her own feelings, she soon finds that the memories of Humphrey's former romances remain alive and well within the halls of his sprawling, old-world manor, which has fallen into a state of disrepair, I might add. One particular presence is most famously felt in the stairwell portrait of Humphrey's late and most recent wife—his seventh wife, in fact. Now, the enchantingly eerie and equally iconic portrait, referred to in the film as the Portrait of Jacqueline, was painted by studio contract artist Calvin Joyce as a favor to Dandridge for an early morning pickup following a rowdy steak dinner at Herman's in Hollywood. Joyce also painted the portrait of the Osborne Family's beloved spotted setter Tilly from the 1948 Robert Robinson production *Caring for Tilly*. And would go on to supply the paintings for former SS officer in South American hiding, Jürgen Maxwell, in 1966's *A Saunter Over a Certain Ridge*. Paintings that, interestingly enough, were bought in the 1970s by an anonymous Argentine art collector.

Now, it was while in production on *Red Alley* two years earlier when producer Roy B. Dandridge was handed a copy of the book by his mistress as a cautionary gesture. Dandridge was spellbound by the story. Particularly the designer's obsession, often conveyed through a series of long, transfixed gazes during the character's many late-night reveries portrayed so poetically in the novel. Jack Humphrey's striking, silent screen presence was a no-brainer. Dandridge campaigned for months seeking the rights to the property. And despite the studio's eagerness, there was one holdout—the book's author, Dorothy Addison—who, by 1952, was invalid and confined to her West Sag home. Dandridge wined and dined the bed-stricken author, preparing her a lavish tray of prescribed delicacies nestled next to the studio's offer and a pen, which Dandridge held for the weak and dying novelist—who, at the time, was too ill even to speak. Production began the following week with a script that was already being developed behind the scenes by screenwriter Sam Stevens. Stevens had previously penned the film adaptations for *Muybridge Station* and *Where Crimson Wings Fall* in 1948, both under Cowen. The former features a young Elliot Rennie, who appears in the film we're about to see. It's a small role and arrives early, but Rennie's signature snappy cadence is well-represented here as Ritter's editor. Not to mention Stevens's original script for *Marry the Blond!* from 1953, of which he took home the Oscar, just one year before Wetherby Manor—which Stevens, in his later life, admitted was his favorite and most stimulating script.

And for those of you spending the day with us, we just finished watching *Pangs of Lilith*—Dandridge's third and final film with Barbara Ritter, coming in 1957. Their first collaboration, however, was in 1950 with *Caged Saddle*, the film-noir western which received four Oscar nominations, including best picture and best cinematography for Cecil Beers—which we have on the schedule for later this month here on Stewart Classic Films. So, when *The Ghosts of Wetherby Manor* came up, Dandridge didn't have to think too hard on his leading lady.

In due time, Ritter's and Humphrey's characters fall passionately in love—culminating courtesy of what is easily considered the film's most memorable romantic scene, with Ritter and Humphrey's iconic terror-soaked embrace and trembling kiss against the rocky cliff shore and towering ocean spray that surrounds them as Ritter's character cycles through the various presences that seem to be compelling her. A scene made even more vivid by the film's haunting score, provided by the great Leonard Mosby—whose work on Wetherby Manor earned him the Oscar. And rightly so. His spectral and other-worldly arrangements remain an equal and lasting element of the film, conjured in most cases by a mere mention of the film's title.

Considered one of the greatest on-screen kisses of all time, the scene took over nine months to shoot and was a miserable experience for the two actors. Ritter later told gossip queen Mamie Dickers that what appears on the surface as her vibrant, rosy complexion is nothing more than what Ritter called "sea-chapped cheeks." And although makeup artist Lonnie Westmore took credit for Ritter's sultry glow in her celebrated industry memoir years later, the reality is that talked about blush was the work of Mother Nature. Dealing with ever-changing weather conditions and an eye for perfection, the film's director, visual master Otto Slazenger, shot over six hundred takes of the immortal kiss using no stand-ins and was photographed entirely on location, busting the long-standing myth that it was shot on a stage using two gaffers.

Throughout his entire career, Slazenger held the reputation of being an authoritarian. A temperament that served the quality of his pictures well. His social game was another story. Known for carrying around town a compact bullhorn which he generally used when speaking to service folk, as well as in every marital bed he shared over the years, Slazenger sacrificed nothing under the authority of his own vision and often held up production for days at a time to partake in meditative reflection. Employing a discipline so intense, Slazenger was pronounced legally dead thrice during the film's production, with the director coming to one of the times only to find himself in a Hollywood morgue. Production resumed that afternoon. The experience would eventually inspire Slazenger's definitive suspense picture, the sardonically titled *Curbside Delivery* in 1961—known by its studio title, *Paralysis*. However, 1954 was a busy year for Otto Slazenger. In addition to this afternoon's film, he delivered four other pictures that same year: *Silent Narrator, Celeste* (with Muriel Taylor in the title role), *The Florida City Story*, and *Viva Rio!*

To help explore the dark, subconscious depths of the film's subject matter, Slazenger enlisted the hyper-realistic imagery of surrealist painter Luciano Salamander to design what was pitched to him as an "uncredited dream sequence," to accompany the Dorothy Addison classic. However, his unmistaken themes can't be missed—dripping moons wearing bowler hats, exposed gears, and other mechanical workings in place of facial features. In tandem with extremely long-legged birds and loaves of saturated bread spread across the mansion's nightmarishly long dining room table, where Ritter's character finds herself at one end, seated with the fashion designer's not so long forgotten lovers in a truly terrifying scene; assembled using strobing bursts of brilliant Technicolor and ghostly superimpositions. Images of tarnished silver with a rotten, seemingly endless feast ravished by worms and maggots—loaded with grave symbolism and all the celebrated marks associated with Salamander, laying the groundwork for another unforgettable insistence where Mosby's score shines and accentuates Ritter's psychological torment.

With co-stars Clifton Quinn as the young architect living up the shoreline, as well as Eleanor Fain, Vivian Patrick, and Libby Hoyt— each of whom, before the events of the film, met a tragic fate following their time with the eccentric fashion designer. And featuring a fresh-faced, up-and-coming June Thatcher in only her second role, years before finding small screen fandom with *The June Thatcher Show* in 1962; which was followed by a number of less successful title series: *It's June* in 1968, *June* in 1975, and *What Now, June?* in 1984. But, in the film coming up, Thatcher plays Ritter's kid sister home from college for the summer, who's invited up to Maine for the week to visit her sister and meet, of course, her new love interest. It doesn't take Thatcher long to realize something's up with sis. An assertion confirmed during her famous afternoon stroll with Ritter and a feverish scene high above the crashing waves where Ritter's character slowly and inexplicably grabs her sister by the shoulders and leans her carelessly over the cliff's edge after Humphrey's character displays an immediate attraction to Thatcher. It's a scene of sheer panic, brought to life by an exceptional performance by, at the time, a virtually unknown Thatcher. Though with her first role as Rosalind Shaw's kid sister in the musical comedy *Forever Sweetheart*, released just one month before Wetherby Manor, Thatcher had already proven promising, to say the least. But it would be her role in today's film that provided the young talent with her breakout performance.

And like their possession-fueled, on-screen vying for Humphrey's affection shown later in the film, tension between Ritter and Thatcher quickly spilled over onto the set when the production's publicity began favoring the newcomer over the seasoned star. *Forever Sweetheart* was a box office success for Cowen and featured two scenes that were a hit with, well, college males. Firstly, an innocent scene in the kitchen where Thatcher is squeezing lemons and gets some in her eye. A hilarious gag reused in the time-honored grapefruit episode of *The June Thatcher Show*, which was modified due to Cowen's ownership of the lemon use. And secondly, a scene with Thatcher doing vocal mouth exercises during a finishing school pronunciation course. Fan letters flooded the Cowen mailroom, and June Thatcher was fast-tracked into the marketing buzz of Wetherby Manor.

The film's most sensual scene, featuring Thatcher in a nightgown standing in the moonlight of Humphrey's bedroom, was, unlike her previous work, subject to a great deal of scrutiny from the censors. It wasn't the nightgown they took issue with, but the warm glass of milk Thatcher is holding. When viewed under the microscope of the production code, the milk, and its position near Thatcher's bust, was seen as suggestive.

Working closely with set designer Bess Linder and director of photography William Howl, Slazenger found a particularly, well, creepy technique for isolating Ritter and Thatcher from their backgrounds as they lose more and more of themselves to the unseen spirits of Humphrey's past while the film progresses. All of which is complemented brilliantly with Ritter and Thatcher being draped in moldy, deteriorated evening gowns by costume designer Susan Sellers. A decision that initially didn't sit well with the film's producer, Roy B. Dandridge, who didn't take to the idea of his female lead or her young co-star looking, at one point in the film, like a quote: "stained porcelain swamp goon heading to the spring formal."

Also worthy of mention is the film's significant title sequence by illustrator and optical effects artist Louise Blair—who, by the end of her career, had designed a total of five opening credit sequences for Otto Slazenger, including *Long Distance Murder, The Cunning Mr. Webster Wallace,* and *A Short Ride Through Liberty County,* with Jimmy Brennan in 1962.

Aided by the vast and stunning photography of William Howl, along with camera operator Earl Laughton—my first cousin two generations removed—the old mansion and its surrounding landscape, together, serve as arguably the film's central character, with much of its sweeping day-for-night exteriors covered entirely by the 2nd Unit, with Nathan Russell at the helm. Film loader Dickie Rascus, whose work on other notable productions, *Shadows in Heat* and the Gloria Andrew's comedy *Ain't Fame Funny?* in 1951, would go on to work with Earl Laughton, alongside 1st Eugene Edmunds, on every film after Wetherby Manor; until a falling out in 1979, following an 800-foot mag of licorice fed through the camera on Richard Barris's production of *Space Safari.* One of those legendary Hollywood tales, with Edmunds as the saboteur. Payback for Rascus and Laughton stealing Edmunds's hat and holding it above his head before hanging it on a street post during the trio's triple-date with the Lana Sisters—

which took several weeks to arrange. And, yep, this one happened, all 800 feet of it. Up till their deaths, each occurring in the same year, 1987, the three would maintain separately that Wetherby Manor was their proudest work.

During the film's gripping climax, while a freak storm rips the manor apart, shingle-by-shingle, stone-by-stone, during what can only be explained as the meteorological manifestation of Humphrey's hauntings, it's Clifton Quinn's character as the neighbor that saves Ritter and her sister, leaving the prominent dressmaker to the rubble remains of which he created. Now still and silent. With best boy duties from Pat Wade and a Cowen front office girl, who prior to the production had been with the studio for several years, but by the time Wetherby Manor rolled around, was looking for something new.

In the end, Ritter returns to New York to finish the feature and move on with her life, putting the entire episode behind her. With surprises around every corner, filled with shocking twists and plot points mentioned here in their entirety, by Cowen Pictures—with script supervisor Marilyn Heathrow and catering by Hot Box Meals of Hollywood—from 1954... *The Ghosts of Wetherby Manor.*

A Lap Around Montefino

*G*areth Byrum once equated a lap at Montefino to a running of the bulls, if it were held in some shop with a lot of fragile things; porcelain, maybe, but by a different name—historic, picturesque, glamorous, romantic, and fraught with peril. Malcolm Holloway described it as dicey at its most controlled. Benito Moretti called it foolishly reckless before his tragic death at the acclaimed circuit in 1971. "A race that would be outlawed, stripped from the calendar, if not for its prestige," said Spanish racing superstar Antonio Flores. In fact, the only thing to warrant the danger of Montefino is a victory at Montefino. A feat awarded only to perfection.

Since 1926, the world's top drivers have gathered on the scenic shores of the Italian Riviera for the most prestigious race in all of motorsport. Hobnobbing with the world's wealthiest and social elite, the once small fishing village of Montefino is the crown jewel of road racing disciplines across the globe, from touring cars and GT to the open-wheel formulas, which are part of a multi-tiered program governed by the International Motorsport Association. Here, young racing talents show off their skills and climb the ranks from Delta through Beta, chomping at the bit for a seat in the premier echelon, Formula Alpha—motorsport's preeminent racing series. And on the fourth Sunday in August, arguably the biggest stage in all of sports—the Montefino Grand Prix.

With the 83rd running of the prominent race a mere week away, traditionally held on the final day of the Montefino Biscotti Festival, the city is buzzing with excitement. By land, air, and sea, hundreds of thousands pour into the exclusive resort town of the microstate capital by the same name, in the Italian region of Tuvoli, by the Ligurian Sea. It is an atmosphere like none other.

At 2.46 miles, consisting of twenty turns, with minimal overtaking opportunities, the Circuito di Montefino runs on closed city streets and takes nearly a month and a half to set up—barriers, curbs, even the grounds for the popular Biscotti Garden, where biscotti and racing fans alike purchase wristbands for an unlimited sampling of the area's famous nut and seed infused biscuits. Team principal for the privateer Nielsen-Wilhelm racing team, Scott Wilhelm Jr., stated that in their nine years of running the Grand Prix—with nine retirements resulting from reliability issues, contact, or a course streaker in 2004—the glazed cinnamon raisin biscotti remains a deliciously sweet consolation. Still, all eyes remain fixed on the circuit, the true star of the weekend. Revered sportswriter and racing enthusiast Dameon Higgins once wrote: "Start-to-finish, high and low, on the inside and the out, hard on the brakes or flat out, it shimmers in the golden light running off the sea, thousands of kilometers of myth and magic, the immortality of Montefino."

Sector 1

A lap around the legendary street circuit begins with a short sprint off the grid along the vibrant Camerone Viale in the heart of Montefino's commercial district—home to extravagant designer labels like Conti, Portière, and Bruno Gallo, who turned heads at Milan Fashion Week earlier this year with their cargo turban worn by Czech supermodel Martina Sedlák. An accessory that style consultant Michael Costa called "elegant and practical." Rumors leading into race week have the 2018 Model of the Year painting the town Billari red on the arm of Jannik Richter, three-time German World Champion and closed-toe sandals designer—whose recent creation, the men's Yak hair hoof, was shown off in a St. Petersburg-staged collaboration with yacht-chic, linen-master Benjamin Tweed. Racing down the champion's esplanade, drivers jockey for early position before the high-speed, sweeping left-hander up the iconic La Cappella Rossa Curve, named after the cafe situated at the base of the hill.

Known for their fish stew and horseradish clam coolers, the owner of La Cappella Rossa, Berenice Catalano, eagerly awaits the influx of racing teams and tourists. "Every night's a celebration," she says. And to anyone nursing a hangover or looking to start off a proper day of spectating on the right foot, she recommends the same to everyone: Cappella Rossa's hearty breakfast drink made with white wine and fish stock, a whole prawn, bay leaves, a dash of black pepper, and a spritz of seawater for the soul—as well as any lingering mouth sores, as Montefino's party scene runs rampant with carefree tendencies. And with every drink comes an official kiss from the eighty-seven-year-old restaurateur and town treasure. Patrons are made aware of the cafe's full-lip service by a somewhat shrine of a sign above the bar, hanging next to a black-and-white photo of Bunny—as the locals know her—at age fifteen, winning the 1948 title of Miss Montefino.

Climbing 41.3 meters at an 18% gradient, Cappella Rossa ascends through the narrowing streets of the Old Town as residents crowd the balconies of their brightly colored houses lining the road. A deafening couloir of cheers and high-octane racing seizes the senses as spectators watch the field of racers charge up the hill under their feet. Vibrations and bursts of engine and throttle shake the foundations of the centuries-old structures.

On the opening lap of the 1971 Grand Prix, British driver Ian Matcher—after starting at the back of the grid due to a brush with the wall in qualifying—made up eight positions off the start before flying up Cappella Rossa flat out; this, in an era when lifting off the throttle into Turn 1 was vital. Somehow miraculously keeping his Yokota Camera-sponsored BV-71 Extra out of the barriers and remarkably gaining three more positions, Matcher later stated that a bee trapped inside his helmet caused him to miss his deceleration mark. The 1966 Montefino victor and World Champion managed to muster twelve tours around the circuit before retiring from the race with numerous bee stings to the face, swelling his eyes virtually shut. The following year, Matcher returned to the Montefino coast wearing a black-and-yellow-striped fire suit with stinger and matching helmet. It bore a distinctive signature on the back: "The Four-winged Devil." Unfortunately, Matcher would receive his second consecutive DNF in the north of Italy after his commemorative stinger proved an unmanageable discomfort, which the team could not remove due to a contractual agreement with Golden Maker's Honey.

After cresting Cappella Rossa, drivers enter a heavy-braking zone for the 100-degree right-hand corner of Sant'agnella, named for the church sitting just back from the barriers. Its landmark bell tower still stands tall over the Old Town. Although the main building today is chiefly used for the church's lucrative production of rosary beads. Handcrafted to varying sizes, these religious Montefino staples are the work of two Vatican-sanctioned crafters putting in a grueling sixteen-hour work week. The Sant'agnella beads are praised for their prayer properties, boasting an impressive answered-to-non-answered response ratio. Before every race, Bishop Ezio de Pisa gathers with the locals at sunrise to pray for the safety of the drivers—and their girlfriends, as the annual allure of Montefino brings out to the circuit both the wives and the girlfriends.

In 1986, the wife of driver Oliver Graham and his then-girlfriend engaged publicly in a bare-knuckle brawl in the center of the Piazza del Mare after running into one another wearing the same gifted couture jacket by Labelle. The scrap escalated when Italian reporter Silviana Nucci, wielding a wired microphone, entered the monument-roped ring sporting her own high-sewn, white denim customization by the French designer—a known style worn and celebrated by Graham throughout his career. The racing and fashion worlds alike called him "The White Denim Wizard" because, in addition to his fashion sense, his style of racing seemed sorcery.

This flattering handle became the premise for the 1985 choose-your-own-adventure book, *The Endless Race,* by acclaimed children's author P.D. Pennyback. Readers follow the three-hundred-year-old, white-clad wizard and five-time Formula Alfa World Champion, Oliver Graham, trapped in a never-ending, fantasy-set Montefino Grand Prix, controlled by a malevolent entity in the sky with a skull for a face, causing accidents and creating obstacles brandished from their orb-infused scepter.

Murmurs ran through the 1993 paddock when actress Sandra Mickles, girlfriend of Brazilian phenom, Edson Sosa, was poisoned with a powerful stool softener while dining at the waterside Ristorante La Luna. Sosa's wife at the time, Catalina Marseille—although not legally given the ongoing marriage annulment to former grid girl Genevieve Styles—was suspected of administering the colon cocktail after an engineer from the American Jack Ralph Racing team noticed Ms. Marseille at the restaurant that evening, making out with a busboy by the bathroom.

After Sant'agnella, it's back on the gas for the slight uphill straight with a fortified left-hand kink known as Castle. Formally, the Castle Straight, runs along the towering stone wall of Montefino's eight-hundred-year-old Castello Delle Armi perched on the hillside. Built by the Ossani family in 1347, after obtaining the land in the trade of a slightly used goat and what local historians call "aggressive inbreeding," the castle remains the oldest structure in all of Tuvoli. With the right-hand side of the racing surface sloping toward the sea, a break in the buildings creates a wondrous view of the city and marina below before the straight's famed high-speed bend brings racers mere centimeters from the castle wall.

Per tradition, spectators use color chalk to draw and write messages on the fortress stones. This year, many of the pastel sentiments bid farewell and thanks to the Finnish Finisher, the Finn to win, Heikki Mäkinen, driving in his final Montefino Grand Prix. Mäkinen holds the Formula Alpha records for both consecutive starts and driving the furthest without the use of hands—an achievement that stands unrivaled at a distance of four laps around Dellarga. A full three tours more than Hugh Nevin's astounding 1979 final lap at the equally distant Wellington Park. A lap that witnessed the Blustery Brit prodding around the course at a crawl in his number sixty-six Lee Jackman entry, stuck in fifth and with two dislocated shoulders, navigating the turns by frantically pounding his head against the steering wheel.

In 1987, fans awoke on race day to find on the castle wall a large map detailing the whereabouts of the fabled lost treasure of Count

Giuseppe Sisco. Youngster teammates Wesley Pratt and Giovanni Lorenzo from team Lottora—the Belgian wafer company and three-time winner of the World Constructors' Championship—continued their battle off the track, trying to outwit one another to the loot's location. After several other racers and a hat full of engineers missed the Grand Prix entirely courtesy of a humorous collection of brave and bumbling escapades, it was later revealed that the map was merely a promotional campaign for a new beachside liqueur bar on the other side of the peninsula—The Spritz Shack.

Out of Castle, drivers blast uphill once again, passing under the single-span Larino arch bridge—where Duke Mafeo VIII, the Wiggler, sister-cousin and brother-in-law to Oliverio III, the Docile, was hung by the neck after laying with someone from outside the family—before the second gear, off-axis, right-hander of Scrutto to complete Sector 1. At the highest point on the circuit, fifty-six meters above the lowest point, Turn 4 Scrutto is considered today the first of only a few overtaking opportunities on these storied streets. Locking oneself to the gearbox of the driver ahead allows challengers to slingshot their racing craft around the outside, through the exit of Castle, and position themselves for an inside line.

Although a straightforward pass in the modern V6 turbo-hybrid era—or for that matter, the 1992 and 1993 seasons, which welcomed robotic arm braces and self-steering cars to eliminate driver fatigue—in 1975, more nerve was needed when the dashing and daring American driver, Eric Smits, did it famously on two wheels. Known for his tail-happy, elbows out style of racing, the blonde-haired ex-surfer and 1974 Logs Magazine centerfold—August issue—made a late lunge into Scrutto and was squeezed on the inside by his championship rival and lead Bellari driver, the wild South African, Danie Jordaan. Smits caught the curb and pitched the right side of his Jack Ralph TR-1 machine into the air in spectacular fashion. Acclaimed Formula Alpha photographer, Sid "Sidney" Lubo, captured the incredible moment through the lens of his camera. Upon closer examination, the photo revealed the racing heartthrob gesturing to Jordaan with his middle finger while completing the pass with half his wheels off the road.

Sector 2

Sector 2 of the celebrated Montefino street circuit begins with a downhill plunge through the wooded Montefino Botanical Gardens and Turns 5, 6, 7, and 8, aptly named the Garden S's. One of the city's most visited tourist sites and home to twenty-four hundred different species of plants—including the first-ever fish-flower hybrid, known by its scientific name, Vincenzo—the Giardini Botanici Montefino remains one of the circuit's more historically significant sections.

During the victorious 1936 drive of Jans Gruber, who raced under the flag of Nazi-controlled Germany, der Führer himself was on hand for the momentous 10th anniversary of the renowned race. He delighted crowds from his convertible Wisserflieger and gloated over the Reich's motorsporting superiority. While visiting the gardens with his entourage and two German shepherds, Charlie and Fritz, the daunting dictator was approached by a polish groundskeeper for not picking up his dogs' droppings. With cameras flashing, the head of state gripped his ceremonial riding crop and, without expression, removed the waste using a large banana plant leaf. Hitler historians and acclaimed Western war documentaries state emphatically that this exchange sent the Führer into a two-year-long stew, which he rectified on September 1, 1939.

A slice of serenity removed from the bustling city, this fast and tricky downhill section, now asphalt, was made even more treacherous in the race's early runnings as the original surface was brick, built by a mandatory youth works project called Minors for Montefino. Repaved in 1960, drivers float through the esses with unmatched agility at breakneck G's, dancing from apex to apex with rhythmic precision.

It was here, in 1981, Cyril Levine famously lapped his Gilbert teammate and second-place runner, Mario Gasparini, humiliating him to the point of permanent impotence.

Sam Hurley lost the 1959 Grand Prix on the final lap in Turn 7 when the steering column broke on his emblematic Ragatti Angel— glistening in its signature matte blue with white wings stretched across the fuel cell. This, the first entry in what would become a decades-long fleet for the French manufacturer. The Carl King-designed, alcohol-guzzling Angel was sent careening through the hay bales and straight into the Queen Claudia Greenhouse. It came to rest at the Heart of the Inca exhibit—a species of flower that blossoms with brilliant red and yellow when it reaches one hundred years old, which it did against the crash helmet of Sam Hurley before its immediate death in dazzling tangerine. A photo of the pair found itself on the front page of the Gazzetta di Montefino, as well as a watercolor depiction inside Ronan O'Shea's sterling publication of botanical illustration—from which Hurley's family still receives royalties.

Exiting the esses, it's a short straight into the tight right-hander of Flammia, named for the nearby historic hillside L'Hotel Flammia—a favorite hideout for A-list celebrities, B-list nobility, and C-list lounge singers. That is unless guests are lucky enough to catch electrical guru Dennis Bertelkamp, from team Asparna, tickling the ivories to the soothing stylings of two-time World Champion and notable karaokist Mace Rue—who, during the off-season, took third place in a 24-hour Tokyo legends competition for solo adult Contempo. Constructed in the mid-18th century by Baron Domenico Flammia in the Baroque style, the hotel and surrounding cliffside have been passed down through the generations.

Today they're overseen by popular Montefino playboy Stefano Flammia, the 5th Baron—a title no longer recognized by the state but covered by the tags on his collection of classic Bellaris, each of which he can be spotted driving around town with his hair down. Travel writer Lawrence Conrad describes the chance encounter as "a streamer of silver magnificence blowing in the wind." Draped daily in a red velvet suit with his signature walking stick of gold embellish and maraschino stain, Stefano—as labeled by his flamboyant embroideries—is accredited by most for Montefino's glitzy and wild, playground atmosphere.

It's an ambiance perfected over the years inside the rowdy and promiscuous L'Hotel Flammia—from the raunchy wedding reception of noted fashion photographer Sebastian Tremblay and Romanian tennis star Nadia Dumitrescu, which consisted of a two-hundred-thousand-euro white truffle caviar food fight, to the ritualistic orgies hosted monthly by master of ceremonies and renowned art dealer Thayer Dorffule. Although none more legendary than the great team Jib-Jib orgy that resulted in the 1991 citywide linen scare and fumigation.

The Flammia Hotel is a must for anyone seeking those wayward Montefino nights with hedonistic pursuits. Pleasures that are surely satisfied with an invite up to the notorious presidential suite, where guests and partygoers alike receive an optimal vantage point of the Montefino fireworks display, marking the end of race week. A sight Italian journalist and formula groupie, Gabriele de Marco, described as: "Where Heaven meets Earth in bursts of stimulating radiance. A spectacle two-fold, gleaming from water pure in spiritual grandeur. Now let me tell you about the fireworks show."

Clean out of Flammia, drivers shift up for the flowing high-speed double left-hander known as Promontory, meaning headland. This narrow and nerve-racking sixth gear dive connects drivers to the densely forested ridge of the Venturella Headland and State Park, the most isolated and visually spectacular section of the circuit.

During a soaked 1956 Montefino Grand Prix, the Bavaria-born specialist Dieter Krause—on debut for the dominating Honolulu-based manufacturer, Palakiko—had a dreadful start when he stalled his Palakiko factory front-engine 181 Macadamia Special on the grid. Miraculously, Krause found grip where no other driver could and, in the opening few laps, pulled himself up through the field in horrendous conditions to take the lead from his teammate and number one driver, Ano Likeke—the Polynesian Prince of Paradise Town. Within the same lap, in a race where the rate of attrition gave the appearance of an endurance slugfest, Krause put in an astounding twenty seconds between him and his second-place teammate. And yet, on the following lap, Krause was given team orders to slow on the exit of Promontory and let Likeke pass, even though Likeke was considerably slower and leading the championship by an astonishing one hundred points.

A German driver in an all-Hawaiian team with a Hawaiian sponsor (Trader Tiki—producers of the successful Mai Tai in a can), Krause served as the team's optical foreigner, seated to stifle talk of national bias. Brought in as the T-car, or the third car, Krause was demoted to the F-car a few days before the Grand Prix. The modest and soft-spoken German respected his freshman status within the organization and followed orders, dropping behind his Empress's Sweet Rolls-endorsed team leader. On the back foot, Likeke struggled for pace and, out of the last turn on the final lap, ran out of fuel. Krause went to overtake for the victory but, once again, was ordered by his team to assist Likeke by pushing him across the finish line. Behind the pair, their Palakiko teammates, Kai Māhoe and Iakopa Kaiwi, crossed the line in third and fourth.

After the race, Palakiko team boss, Liam Hale, instructed Krause to voluntarily notify the IMA stewards that he knowingly gained an advantage during the Grand Prix by wearing a seatbelt and helmet with padding. As a result, the IMA disqualified Dieter Krause from the race and suspended him for the rest of the season, while his Palakiko teammates made up the '56 podium. After the trophy ceremony, Hale introduced the triumphant Likeke to Krause's stunningly statuesque girlfriend, Ophelia Antonelli—acclaimed Italian stage and film actress and Academy Award winner for her supporting role in 1955's *The Summer Terrace*. Likeke and Antonelli wed later that month and moved into a Hawaiian plantation-style home on the outskirts of Oahu, which Krause bought on the authority of Palakiko team orders.

After Promontory, it's another dodgy downhill dash to perhaps the most iconic turn in motorsport—the Moreno Hairpin. Like the 16th at Myers Creek or the Devil's Mistress in Virginia, the Moreno Hairpin transcends the racing world, drawing in outsiders with its beauty and mystique. With drivers rolling through in first gear at a mere 40 kph, this 180-degree curve is the slowest corner on the calendar and points away from the city on entry, offering a breathtaking tree-lined vista of the eastern coastline and a one-hundred-meter drop to the waves and rocks below.

Originally named the Borroni Hairpin after Italian driver Eduardo Borroni threw his 1.5-liter supercharged Volari 1-11 over the unprotected edge in 1947, the name was changed in 1952 when Antonio Fanucci perished trying to overtake Louis Bisset on the outside, dropping his left-rear and catapulting him over the side. The Fanucci Hairpin stood without challenge until 1958 when British driver, Leslie Bernhard, lost his brakes coming out of Promontory, launching his P7 Herbert Lauder Unicorn nearly five hundred yards into the sea. A maneuver that posthumously earned him the record for furthest distance jumped in a Formula car. In '59, the Bernhard Hairpin became the Pritchard Hairpin. And in '63, the Azarola Hairpin. '67 saw the Patel Hairpin. Then, the McLaughlin, the Turnbull, the Ward-Parker, and the Team Ráscal Hairpin in 1970, when all three drivers for the Canadian Ráscal Racing lost their lives after running a nose-to-tail procession right off the cliff.

In 1971, a guardrail was installed to prevent future fatalities. Then, removed the following year due to an impeded view.

The splendor of the scenery so entranced the hairpin's most recent victim and namesake, nineteen-year-old Colombian driver Alejandro Moreno—a Formula Alpha rookie that rocketed up through the ranks after dominating the '93 Formula Delta season—that he drove straight through his braking point and skidded off the side while snapping a photo. Miraculously, Moreno survived the tumble thanks to a group of fishermen that pulled him from the sinking wreckage after casting their nets. Following his incredible recovery, Moreno retired from racing and introduced to the area Montefino's premier fishing and formula experience—perfect for tourists; complete with souvenir tuques, a captivating retelling of his brush with death (including all thirty-two points of contact with the rock face), and a comprehensive workshop on traditional Mediterranean methods for catch-and-release octopus.

Barreling back down toward sea level, hugging the inside slope, it's a quick flick to the right into the Turn 12 bend, where stock car and oval-specialist turned Montefino hopeful Danny Ellison slammed into the outside barriers after being caught out by a right turn. Immediately following Turn 12—which, despite having no official name, has over the years been labeled by writers and commentators as "No Name"—drivers are hard on the brakes for the fast and funneling second or third gear left-hander of Rudolfo. The Rudolfo Bridge takes drivers over the charming residential canal of the same name before blasting back into town, completing Sector 2. Designed as a waterway for prostitutes in the 1600s, the Canale di Rudolfo is still to this day controlled by the Il Segreto di Sant'Agostino Brothel, or St. Augustine's Secret. Positioned on the western bank as a central launching point for courtesans, the cherished Montefino institute has been favored for centuries by the townspeople for its waterside service.

Sector 3

The final sector of the Circuito di Montefino kicks off as drivers reenter town, rushing down Della Croce through the center of the city, kicking up dust and swirling debris—Lottora wrappers and empty bags of Calamari Crisps. Drivers shift up through the gears before flinging their machines to the left into Turn 14, the famed Biscotti Bank. Just off from the lively Biscotti Garden and world-famous Biscotti di Montefino factory, fans pack the sacred grounds of biscotti master Alessio Bartoli as racers flash by in seventh gear entering the fastest part of the circuit. Referred to in the region as cantucci, Montefino is synonymous with biscotti.

Its origins date back to 1905 when local baker, Alessio Bartoli, opened a small shop along the town's main thoroughfare where he offered two versions of his flavorful biscuits—plain and mint sardine. They were cherished equally. Over the years, these tasty treats gained global notoriety, inspiring both North American and Asian variations, each featuring sausage and ketchup. Today, the factory produces over one hundred different varieties shipped worldwide—from mashed cherry pit paste to their praised smoked eggs with in-shell pine nuts. In addition, visitors to the factory will find a preserved bottle of Saltarini Vino Santo; the same wine Bartoli used to soak a sample from his first batch of twice-baked history after it proved too dry for human consumption—a formula that remains unaltered after a hundred years.

In the factory cellar, there sits, set back in the limestone foundation of the Montefino Rock, a heavily guarded walk-in steel vault a meter thick and housing the Bartoli secret recipe of flour, eggs, and sugar, along with their original 1905 starter yeast—famous for its complex makeup of bacterial flora and volcanic ash from the catastrophic eruption of Mount Puzzinelli in 1798. The factory heightened security in 1959 after a group of professionals was hired by a rival biscotti company from the south of Italy to penetrate the vault and extract the priceless starter dough. The heist culminated with a fabled getaway aided by a tricolored squad of enclosed Rosari scooters (green, white, and red), cutting through narrow alleyways and down the hallowed steps of Francesco into the crowded Piazza di Galati. The iconic chase was so cinematic it was mimicked in the 1968 British caper *Take the Biscuit and Run!*

Out of the bank, drivers find eighth gear reaching speeds over 290 kph as they break for the sea, bolting toward the marina, fading right-to-left to set up for a quick sixth gear slice through the Cruise Ship Chicane. Here, Brazilian driver Paulo Ferreira collected a train of runway attaché cases under the front wing of his turbocharged P2 Hopper during the 1987 Grand Prix. Ferreira was forced to enter the pits. His crew rushed to clear the front wing of his Striker Airlines racing craft, covered in shaving cream and tangled with floral resort wear. During the '87 broadcast, legendary Formula Alpha commentator James Harvey—the series' authoritative voice for over thirty years, widely known for his signature cadence and seamless puns—pointed out that the owner of the luggage had lavish taste in sleepwear when the English sportscaster successfully identified a tattered set of Alfie Ruskin silk pajamas.

Whizzing by the cruise terminal, drivers blast out of the chicane and speed down the beachside boulevard of Costiero, racing by the exclusive Montefino Yacht Club, constructed in 1953 by Giulio Margherita, the former Marquess of Montefino. Margherita erected the revered establishment to preserve favor with the city after reports uncovered from the war revealed his interests in converting the entire Montefino waterfront into the world's largest drive-in movie theater. His wartime journal, displayed today behind glass inside the club's classy Il Privilegio Ristorante, consists of sketches and poster drawings for movies he imagined would be screened—*Giant Centipede Meets Space Moth, Invasion of the Colossal Beach Bunnies from Crete, Robot Mannequin.*

With two central piers stretching out into the deep blue waters of the Porto di Nettuno, the private social club plays host to a fleet of eight- and nine-figure luxury superyachts. With names like Vittoriosa and Hard Life, these floating mansions are perfect for entertaining either a cast of celebrities or the weekend's royalty. This year, a steady buzz around the marina surrounds the much-awaited mooring of the one-hundred-meter, Turkey-constructed megayacht, Poseidon's Tug—owned by Saudi prince Sami Abboud—on its maiden trip around the world.

In 1996, one week before the Grand Prix, Australian driver and spokesman for Miguel Trujillo Coffee, Jayden King—a celebrated heel and toe ace with a passion for spending—slipped on the deck of his custom Dutch Royal yacht, The Ballast Buster, snapping his ankle. A private investigation into the incident later revealed a disastrous miscalculation from the vessel's crew when they fitted King for deck shoes with an intermediate tread instead of the full wet. King went on to watch the race from the harbor that year on his thirty thousand dollar, forty-five-inch big screen TV.

Approaching the end of the boulevard, drivers slip around the historic Salvi Fountain for Turns 17 and 18, known as the Fountain, or formally, the Fountain Chicane—aka Fountain Square, aka Fountain, aka the Wets. Built as a war memorial to the Italian Navy, this honored symbol of the Montefino Battery has seen a century's worth of waterlogged engines and airborne chassis.

In 1929, Fabio Voleta's silver and red Nibli racing car, which took victory in the inaugural Tangier Rally one month earlier, cartwheeled across the top of the water, fatally injuring Voleta; despite his state-of-the-art knitted racing toboggan. Safety measures, which, at the time, were seen as excessive and considered by most drivers unnecessary. Or, as expressed by British racer and champion horse breeder Lionel Figgins in the *Snellgrove Daily Express*, "roaringly droll;" before being thrown from his personal three-valve 2.0-liter Krempler during a fender bender outside a Woolshire cafe.

The fountain's trident-harpoon mashup—held by the symbolic statue of a lone, weathered sailor with the tail of a merman—punctured the fuel cell of Pierre Dolbert's backup car as it went flying over the Salvi Fountain in an arcing trail of fire in 1949. The Frenchman suffered scratches and a severed pinky toe that plagued the nine-time Formula Alpha race winner for the rest of his competitive career. A period that saw Dolbert take twenty-eight more victories and two World Championship titles.

It isn't all career-ending incidents at the Wets, as proven in 1976 during the late-night victory skinny-dip of Basil Pentecost. After winning the semi-centennial Grand Prix, the Willoughby Racing driver and his girlfriend, Vera Olivares—Brazilian TV host and former video jockey—and their inseparable lifelong friend, Teddy Collinsworth, bared all for a celebratory frolic in the monumental waters of the Salvi. The trio enjoyed a magnum bottle of Chateau Langrené Brut before drunkenly diving into a sack of Jolly Burgers from the chain's first and highly popular European location while sitting naked on the side of the fountain.

After the fountain, drivers squeeze in a quick tap of throttle before navigating a tight line into Turn 19, the penultimate corner. This hairy and often problematic right-hander—due to its elevated exit and barriers that leave little margin for error—is known as the Baths.

Home to the most optimistic of dives to the inside, resulting in a traffic jam collision year after year, the Baths is named for the nearby swimming pool and sea bath complex where four-time World Champion Giuseppe Severino was kidnapped before the 1957 Grand Prix. During his customary pre-race dip, the Montefino resident and race favorite was abducted from his changing tent at the Santa Corso Baths.

The kidnappers—a group of fanatic Yugoslavian rebels with a passion for Formula Alpha and a hatred for the dominating Severino, whose motives, later stated by their leader in the press, were in the interests of "changing up the podium a bit." Seppe, as fans knew him, was dragged into the back of a King's Tobacco truck and taken to the insurgents' hideout in the mountains.

Fortunately for Seppe, the United States' Central Intelligence Agency—posed as a privateer racing team in their first Formula Alpha entry, put in place to take down Severino, whom they mistakenly interpreted as the head of the Belgrade-based organization—witnessed the abduction from their pit stall. The slip-up began back in the states at the hands of a CIA agent, who, in a series of comically advantageous situations, including the serendipitous sting known internally as Operation Gnocchi Overload, managed to convince the agency that he spoke fluent Italian to further his pursuit of a young Langley receptionist by the name of Pantaleoni.

Meanwhile, back in Europe, the small band of Yugoslavian rebels was the target of round-the-clock surveillance from the United States in their investigation of counterfeit radios smuggled out of the socialist states through respective Western channels. After storming the hideout of ex-revolutionaries, agents were able to recover Severino unharmed. They presented him to the paddock just after the start of the Grand Prix, following a very apologetic drive down the mountain.

Unfortunately, his campaign for a third consecutive Montefino victory would fall just short, coming across the line in fourth after an inspired drive from three laps down.

However, in all the chaos, the CIA-sponsored racing team of Tito's Corn Chips and Tamale Filler finished the '57 Grand Prix on the second step of the podium; their first of two top-three career finishes—proceedings later labeled as "Tamalegate" by Formula Alpha journalist Morris Patterson. Their second podium came in 1981 during surveillance of the suspect Soviet Union-backed Afghan Racing team, whose cars had solid red liveries with a hammer and sickle on the nose.

The final turn of the esteemed circuit, Anita Visconti, or A. Visconti, racers are met with another tight and tricky right-hander bringing them back onto the finish-start straight of Camerone Viale while avoiding a significant bump in the middle of the racing line.

Named for the wife of the race's original organizer in 1926 after she remarked to her husband that the city would make for the site of a magnificent race, it was here Austrian rally champ Lukas Muller was released from his two-year contract with the British racing squad Radford Motors after getting sideways on the exit of A. Visconti, as he had been doing all weekend. Looking cool but losing valuable time, the team fired Muller on his penultimate tour of the circuit during the 1978 Grand Prix, informing him via the pit board on the front straight, next to a pile of his personal effects.

On the final lap, the hardheaded, drifting motorsport veteran from the hills pulled off onto the escape road at Turn 1 and parked his machine outside La Cappella Rossa Cafe. He went inside, sat down at a table with fans, and ordered a krügerl of Zwinkelmizer before asking Bunny to change the radio to the Group C match-up of the Schrozberg AU Club and the EKC Linzer Bulls on home ice.

Twenty historic corners, stretching just under four kilometers. A grand coliseum of wheel-to-wheel combat with gladiators of flesh and blood. Win or lose, live or die, Montefino endures, enshrined in its landscape.

Happy Holidays from the Seaside Club

*I*t's that time of year again. No, not Hep C season. Which for most runs from spring break through summer vacay, but 'round here it's the gift that keeps on givin' all year long. That's right, you know it, I'm talkin' about the holidays, which are officially in full swing. And we know that's a word that gets a lot of play in here. Welcome, all you hard-bodied snow buddies, to the Seaside Club— Carver, California's most hip and happenin' apartment complex in the greater Los Angeles metropolitan area. Located half a block east of the 110, this swinger's paradise is your one-stop shop for carnal pleasure this holiday season.

Built in the 1960s by the Miller Brothers as the premier singles-only apartment building, the Seaside Club, with its two hundred anything-but-discreet units, is both home and playground to L.A.'s sexiest between the ages of sixteen and thirty-five. Only the good-looking need apply—doctors, actors, stewardesses, secretaries, and salesmen that sizzle, each one dripping with holiday cheer. A little punch, a little eggnog, a little late-night cookie for Santa. Keep your snow this season and gimme the sun—poolside, that is—so we can even out those pesky tan lines. It's pink flamingos and palm trees with lights this year and a mouthwatering feast that'll leave you begging for more. And with the festivities about to get underway, it's time for me to slide into my Tad Sebastian designer leisure suit with candy cane stripes and mistletoe belt. Don't wait up this Christmas Eve, 'cause 'round here, there's no such thing as a silent night. You know what I'm talkin' about. So, pour a drink and don't forget the courteous tap on the shoulder if you're lookin' to join in—this is gonna be one holiday celebration you'll never forget.

The first stop on our tour is the always poppin' 4D—the sensual sanctuary of Miss Gladys Adler, stewardess to the stars and a founding member of the mile-high club; still with a seat on the board, if ya catch my drift. Gladys moved into the Seaside in 1969 and has since adopted a tangerine, leather-like complexion that drives all the fellas wild. Her hair resembles an orange whip or summer sidewalk creamsicle—a sunburst veil of bleached hair you can see right through. Its presumed integrity has all the hallmarks of cotton candy reinforced with steel wool. A sophisticated beauty wrapped in green silk and lace and with a taste for Copperfield Slims, this delectable holiday treat titillates her suitors with a provocative proficiency in heart-shaped smoke rings blown from her stoma. Not to mention an oral cavity that, when free of dentures, is as tight as a fucking vice. Her allure is enhanced by an elegant beauty spot on her cheek in the form of a bullet hole from her third husband, Darryl Winston, an adult picture camera operator with a bad temper and a fetish for festive jello molds. She accents the scar with a Vaseline sheen, and when she's fired up and good to go, she rubs it in a circular motion, biting her lip and casting a do-me stare that'll drop all the pants in the room. From there, it's several arousing rounds of connect-the-liver-spots and find-the-right-wrinkle. And with hours of searching ahead of you, there's no doubting this sexy dish of orange sherbet has all the makings of a good time.

We keep this wet and wild winter wonderland going with a stroll by the heart of the Seaside Club—the pool; the place to be and bean-shaped—oh, baby—with high-dive, slide, and a grotto with rocks that, oh, if they could talk. These days, the pool may be scarce of water and home to a collection of shopping carts and used diapers, but it's still a hot spot for the Seaside's most seductive movers and shakers. You know what I'm talkin' about. To and fro. Ungh.

Like Henry Belvedere, our resident snowman that brings on the season's powder. Sniff-sniff. But at a five percent markup. Belvedere's gots to make ends. He slings snow from the clandestine cover of the grotto, which was filled in and made part of the miniature golf course in the late-80s. Belvedere's a tracksuit-clad bronco whose every waking moment resembles a loaded gun if it could talk in competing tempers at the same time. His jet-black jerry curl doo is a semblance of steadfast style punctuated by nylon and leather house shoes. Like Santa, this holiday snowman's going door-to-door, to collect. Who's that rapping on the door? Why, it's the snowman, *lookin' fo' the money you owe! CANDY AIN'T FREE!*

Down the path of discarded bikini bottoms, bloated cigarette filters, and seasonal syringes, it's the red-hot, smokin' tiki barbecue pit. Now a flaming garbage bin next to a busted-up chain-link fence, where, tonight, we're roasting more than just chestnuts. Mmmm— Ptooey. Who ordered the kabob? Two skewers. Three's company for this holiday luau, where some lucky Christmas ham's gettin' stuffed and garnished from both ends.

And ready to take the reins is former child actor Derek Crenshaw from the hit 1970s television series *Six of One.* Derek hasn't had a gig in over two decades and spends most of his days standing on various street corners with noticeable jitters and full-bodied tremors. Ooh, baby. His arms are covered in a trail of track marks and bruises, giving his skin a dazzling lilac hue, highlighted by a festive glitter 'stache from huffing tubes of holiday glue. With hair that can only be described as harboring several species of parasite, this platinum, silver-belled Cali babe can go until sunup and stay awake for seven days straight. His is a party fueled by holiday cheer, copious pills, and enough hatred for his parents to power every Christmas tree in the western United States. Whew, it's gettin' hot over here.

Assuming the position of red-nosed and oh-so randy, in a puffy grey parka with a soiled set of stuffed antlers, is that southern slice o' sweet potato pie folks 'round here call Harmony—a nineteen-year-old runaway with less-than-moderate guitar skills and a prominent standing with the Las Vegas mole people.

And joining them in their out-of-sync, pa-rum-pum-pum—ungh, get some—is Derek's longtime friend of six months, Jim, whom he met under the pier and did hand stuff. These three put the rock in rockin' around the Christmas tree. You know what I'm talkin' about. Just add water, baking soda, and a little heat. Oooh, that burns. No need to wrap these Yuletide tidbits; we're all adults here—consenting. A mouthful of these merry-making morsels will take a frothy mug of mouthwash and three shots of gasoline to cleanse. 'Cause this holiday choo-choo of gnarled and gnawed flesh goes oh-oh-ooooh. Who's that comin' down the chimney? Just a couple o' cream-filled yule logs pumping viscous mirth with a bite of antifreeze. *UNghh, oh, shit.* This is one beauty of a bum fuck you won't wanna miss.

Next, we make our way over to the notorious and oh-so naughty building A, where anything and everything goes. Literally. Where mustache rides run on a continual loop and aviators are mandatory. Where the orgies are legendary, and the oxygen tanks come in a six-pack.

And loitering by the vending machine outside the Seaside's state-of-the-art beauty parlor—now a storage room with multiple padlocks of varying strengths—is the lip-smackin', finger-lickin', sugar plum bombshell of thirty-two, Misty Greene. A resident of 7A—known for its revolving door, if ya catch my drift—Misty's the soon-to-be head waitress down at Toni's Diner, and she's performed fellatio on seven separate customers behind the restaurant when her habit got real bad. This holiday hottie has three kids, substantial alimony, and it shows, especially where it counts, the feet. Ooh, kinky. Misty's got boney bunions that protrude out so much, she has to enter rooms sideways. So, lather up those babies with oil and let ole' Knucks take you downtown, aka Pleasure Town, via St. Sanchez—where the drinks are always dirty. Your guide to tantalizing pedi-delights, with toe-curls and corns by Misty. She's the kinda uninhibited, free-lovin' spirit that'd get freaky with her folds if the price was right, and the needle was pipin'. Cozy up next to a space heater with this peppermint playgirl, and you'll be jonesin' all season long.

We finish off the evening with a festive nightcap inside the dimly-lit sex palace of 6C—home to former accountant extraordinaire Mr. Charlie Farris. But all you surely Seaside honeys out there can call him Chuck. This holly jolly bachelor, draped in wine-colored velour with a crusty dash of puke green and foamy yellow, moved into the Seaside Club last fall after losing both job and family in the wake of a rampant gambling addiction. Whoa, one at a time, ladies. Or not?

Sporting a come-hither combover that covers for days, Chuck spent the last ten months slowly destroying his body inside and out before trying to hang himself from a shoddy light fixture. So, settle in for a steamy winter's night and find out what else is gettin' kissed underneath the mistletoe. Rest assured it'll have the intensity of a walrus kissing a penny. *Reughhhowwwww!*

Illuminated in uneven fluorescent, this straight-up F-pad with a mop ringer, boasts plush bean bag chairs with patches, a chic Christmas pyramid of beer cans, and exposed utilities with a drip-drip—oooooh—that trickles down a calcium buildup. All the same, block out the deafening sound of a grown man crying and climb aboard this sad sack o' holiday spirits and hyper-shingles for one hell of a sloppy sleigh ride.

So, this holiday season, pack in the fun with the swingin' singles from the Seaside Club—saucy, sultry, and oh-so salacious. Let that signature stank be your source for holiday cheer this year, and keep those sleigh bells ringin' all night lon

Reality Minded

*S*ince the early 1960s—with roots in varying artistic and social
movements from Dada and Futurism to interchangeable
forms of abstract expressionism—performance art has
reimagined the relationship between artist and audience. Unlike
theater, where this relationship and the conveyance of emotion are
based in fantasy, performance art challenges reality and its
employment within fine art. It is a conceptual and multifarious
expression that adheres to no particular standard or set of rules.
Therefore, it rejects any definition of itself. It is without boundaries
and can occur in any setting at any time. It can be scripted or
unscripted, live or recorded. It can be as brief as a second or go on for
days. It is truth boiled down, unfiltered, and served in its rawest form.

No postmodern conceptualist has embraced this freeform "anti-
ideology," as it was famously coined by art historian Gary Rosenblatt,
although heavily debated, more than the anonymous performance

street artist known throughout popular culture as Crispin. A master of disguise and human existence, Crispin is considered the godfather of contemporary performance art, with over two thousand works, or "transferences," to his credit.

"Crispin doesn't just perform; he becomes," says abstract art critic Sofie Faye. "He transforms into not an idea, but a reality, and pushes the limits of audience participation. All of whom are unbeknownst to the piece, making it a living, breathing entity. They believe Crispin's identities because he believes the identities and, therefore, the identities are. This is the essence of his art."

With an active career spanning fifty-plus years, the suspected Italy-born artist is believed to have gotten his start in the resorts and playhouses of the Catskill Mountains in the mid-60s. As an actor, the life of the role enamored Crispin, but over time he became disenchanted by the stage's veil of make-believe. When not performing, he began taking on different personas in public—experiments with regard to his studies in people and how they communicate, with an emphasis on existentialism. Lennie Sorrell, entertainment manager for the Grand Palatial Resort outside Majestic Falls, New York, remembers one summer a curious usher named Sam.

"I can still see him in his pressed jacket with gold buttons," Sorrell said in an '87 interview. "Which is odd because we didn't employ ushers. But people seemed to appreciate him, and he loved setting out the chairs."

Crispin is said to have studied fine art at the Windham Ridge School near the hamlet of Seward Corner under the assumed name Arthur Lane, a recorded alias of Nouveau Réalisme painter and photographer Chico Mansard. Here—in addition to partaking in several nonlinear happenings with multiple performers, including *If a Tree Falls...*, in which thirty students wrapped themselves in paper products and stood in the forest amongst the trees for three days drinking cloudy water from bottles labeled "Man"—Crispin performed his indelible Line series, where the young artist took on the role of everyday people standing in lines—army recruiting offices, cafeterias, outside the bathroom at Yankee Stadium. Mounted and entirely silent performances, Crispin, even during this early stage of his life, possessed a sensibility beyond his years. His awareness of the human condition was focused and showed formidable signs of an expressive mastery.

After school, while still in New York, he continued his studies posing as an Italian ice vendor in Central Park, in addition to his work as a haggard gigolo from the South named Adrian, and his first female identity, Kasey Hotchkiss, a union activist for the New York City Snowplow Federation. Hotchkiss held rallies, formed chapters, and uncovered hundreds of cases of corruption throughout major U.S. labor unions and the city of New York—including bribery, fraud, and an inflated salt tax—before her disappearance in 1970. A decade later, in a rare event, Crispin wrote of his time spent working on the untitled Hotchkiss piece.

"It was merely an exercise," Crispin wrote. "A preliminary test to see how deep I could go, past the external, superficial reality of appearance—giving life to the subject's inherent desires. She had friends. And a family. The workers were her family. She made an impact on their lives, and these people would miss her." Even in his experiments, Crispin was redefining art and the audience's emotional involvement.

In 1971, Crispin began his most ambitious project to date. He assumed the role of a marketing guru and heroin addict named Gordon Delahughe. Crispin, as Delahughe, secured a senior position with the Bitterman and Ford firm at East 54th Street and Park, after coming highly recommended from the Sheldon Jameson agency in Chicago, which Crispin concocted during his prep work. He scored junk from the park and lived a fast and empty life in a sterile Manhattan high rise. Crispin—no stranger to the needle since his performance as a burdened dockworker years earlier—managed concentrated doses of the drug before upping his usage. Delahughe was a copy wordsmith and a genius with layouts. He made the firm millions but couldn't kick the demons of an abusive childhood. He pushed his life to the limits in a painful pursuit of value and contentment and, in the end, lost out to his addiction. The Delahughe piece was the conveyance of an urban tragedy, a product of the times, common, presented as a single case in a sea of stories, and it spoke to the public in a profound way.

Word of Crispin's performance spread throughout the art world, and his popularity grew. And with it came wealth, benefactors, and increased notoriety. "The allure of Crispin's identity is part of his message," said contemporary video artist Kyle Close in a 2007 documentary. "He's mythological. His pieces, although lasting, themselves are momentary, fleeting, like all of us. A temporary speck of existence. He is the personification of our condition and the embodiment of our perspective. Biased and based in a culture of our allowing."

By the mid-1970s, Crispin had become a cultural icon. Nobody knew when, where, or who his next piece would be. The public started suspecting anyone in their lives with a murky past of being the famed artist—new acquaintances, longtime friends, even family. He became the conversation. "Are you Crispin?" It was the central question of the 1970s. Early on, Crispin secured his finances through a number of secret accounts using a series of aliases. Sellers filled galleries with articles of clothing from his pieces, each bringing in a small fortune. Entire wardrobes stood in modern art museums throughout America—from the overalls of his bridge painter piece *Billy Fisher* in New York to the knitted sweater of tennis club pro and swinger *Jim Turner* in the San Francisco MoMA. Commissions began pouring in from and to anywhere, anyone that may have known or have had contact with Crispin—people looking to replace someone they had lost, a figure from a dream, even discreet requests from large companies in trouble and seeking a patsy.

Reportedly, in 1977, that song and dance man, Christopher Goldman, tried getting Crispin to appear as the popular comedian at a club in Los Angeles while Goldman himself was performing in New York City.

Financier and art collector Peter Burke placed an ad in the trades for Crispin to appear as a member of the catering staff during his annual preservation society fundraiser. To this day, many art historians believe that Crispin was Peter Burke. Even then, the ethos of Crispin was taking on a life of its own, providing individual conversations on metatheory and the employment of similar practices within the artist's works.

By the start of the 1980s, Crispin had unlimited funds at his disposal. And after years of working on projects with a relatively limited extent, Crispin began his first international piece in the hills of La Punta in northern Sonora as a Mexican drug trafficker for the Los Peños organization. He became Arturo Diaz, a dirt farmer turned producer with a radical new network of shipping routes. In addition, Crispin surgically altered the pigmentation of his skin, giving it a darker, sunbaked complexion to appear as a man of a rural class, to strengthen his backstory.

For two years, Diaz climbed his way up through the ranks from capo to lieutenant and eventually became the number two to Don Juan Carlos Cortez, infamous drug lord and founder of the notorious Los Peños organization. As part of the art piece, to exhibit the volatile nature of the subject, Diaz called a meeting with their southeast rival, the Valencia Cartel, under the pretense of Don Cortez's request. At the meeting, Diaz executed Don Cortez in front of the assembly and assumed control of the operation in a partnership with the Valencia Cartel. A year later, Diaz met his Tijuana bride, with whom he started a family. And in 1986, on the birthday of their youngest, the Mexican Army stormed their seaside villa, killing his family, including his brother, Miguel Juan Diaz—who Crispin contacted years earlier during the piece's planning phase, with a convincing story of their separation at birth. In the following months, the army rounded up the other members of Diaz's crew; but by then, Arturo had vanished without a trace. He remains on the FBI's 50 Most Wanted list.

The *Arturo Diaz* transference remains one of Crispin's most potent and poignant pieces. Heralded as a masterpiece and a daring, unrivaled display of artistic discipline, the project offered a fresh take on the subject of power and greed. In 2002, the Museum of Modern Art in Mexico City placed on display señor Diaz's leather cigarette case in recognition of Crispin's piece, who remains one of the few international artists honored within the institute's halls.

"The cigarette case in Mexico, like personal effects used in Crispin's other works, is not to be confused with the actual piece itself, which has no physical properties," says prominent art critic Maxwell Schmidt. "It is merely a representation of the transference, nothing more. Although, one could argue that the craftsmanship of the case, in addition to its artistic symbolism and significance, does, in fact, hold a market value, but that's not particularly pertinent in this analysis."

The late 80s and early 90s were made up of more contained, ephemeral studies from Crispin, who, by this time, had risen to legendary status. September 1989 saw the untitled Terrence Rogers III project, where Crispin transformed himself into the dimwitted heir to the Rogers Margarine fortune. Rogers dressed daily as a time-traveling space explorer with a silver bomber hat and goggles; a piece now lauded for its conversation on entitlement and its relation to mental health.

In 1991, Crispin took on the life of an anorexic woman named Mary. In preparation, he survived on lemons and hot water, with the occasional honey indulgence. Mary worked at a Baltimore bakery and, through the joy of baking and with the support of her new family of coworkers, rediscovered her self-worth and overcame her disorder. In 2011, Mary's apron was sold at the Weber and Dobbs auction house for $234,000.

Crispin's "100 Days/100 Faces" series ran in San Francisco from October 22, 1993, to January 29, 1994. It consisted of one hundred performances in one hundred days, each a different personality telling its own unique story. Although presented as a collection, notable creations include Dawn Goodspeed, a solo bass player living in the park moonlighting as a streetside peddler of hemp figurines; Bobby, a gay bartender anxious about coming out to his devout parents during an upcoming Christmas visit; and Mr. Rollins, the false name of a beloved city councilman given to a prostitute amidst the early hours of a scandal. As it came to be known, the Faces series is a work of art still evolving some twenty-five years later, as identities from the piece continue to surface through written accounts and word of mouth, with thirty-seven performances still unknown.

"Crispin has turned the art world upside down," wrote art historian Caroline Harden-Smith in her essay "The Beholder of the Eye." "He has completely changed the way we view art, taking it out of the galleries and bringing it into the real world. He's made it accessible. Digestible. Personal. But not without challenge."

Criticism suggesting Crispin was a hoax gained momentum in the late 1980s after the run of his untitled Ashley Robins piece, which found Crispin working in a New York subway token booth for three years. Critics were quick to point out a Crispin timeline that contradicted both his *Electric Cowgirl* piece in Dallas and the *Father O'Malley* project in San Marino, California—confirmed by court transcripts, transfer papers, and payments made by the Catholic church. Doubters of Crispin's legitimacy, spearheaded by the art scene's old guard, publicly discredited his work calling it "a farce with wigs and spirit gum." Still to this day, Crispin supporters argue that the three transferences work in congruence with a larger message and are most likely part of a series, while some Crispin experts believe the debate itself is the actual piece intended by the mysterious street artist.

Over the years, various Crispin imitators have profited from the artist's celebrity, banking on his brand, as well as a few of his more recognizable projects. In 1997, a Santa Cruz artist by the name of Lipsin—known for reproducing Crispin's identities, but as mutes— replicated the iconic performer's celebrated *Side-Pieces* project, where Crispin, as stockbroker Dennis Hale, managed four separate families without their knowledge, comedically, in a conversation about the absurdity of the modern sitcom. Ripsin—a flow-sponsored skateboarder and graffiti artist from Atlanta—remained in a twelve-year state of arrested development as a play on Crispin's 1999 *A Boy's Life* residency, which saw Crispin (who at the time was believed to be in his late sixties) transform into an eight-year-old boy adopted by an unwitting audience of parents. *A Boy's Life*, also known as the Nick Stromberg piece (or Nick Doe), was itself a nod to Brazilian filmmaker Paulo Barbosa and his 1964 film *Senhor Garoto* (or Mister Boy).

The 2000s saw Crispin perform his acclaimed *Puppy Pedigree* transference. Here, he created a local political dynasty by serving as three generations of city councilors for the small Michigan town of Bay Creek. For sixteen years—beginning with the election of Garrett Cocks, followed by the vote of his son Gavin Cocks several years later, then finally his son Grant—Crispin's succeeding identities ruled the board of Bay Creek with iron fists, using the town's funds to develop a state-of-the-art luxury resort on the shores of Lake Michigan for the exclusive use of the wealthy, power elite members of the Cock's cherished Cloak and Dagger secret society from Bowler University. An elaborate commentary on the "ruling and serving classes," as modern art writer Jacob Miller stated, the piece gained international attention when the magazine *Travel and Design* featured the private resort in their "Top Ten Resorts You'll Never Visit." It's widely suspected by fans that *Travel and Design* Editor-in-Chief Isabella Giovanni is another of Crispin's uncredited transferences—in addition to her fiancé, photographer Martin Gould, who went missing while on assignment in Norway.

Today, Crispin is said to be deep in the jungles of Zimbabwe, working on a limited-run twelve-part series focused on the black-market jewelry trade. While some scholars suspect he's living as a writer in upstate Vermont, working on a Crispin biography under the pseudonym Wendra Collins, a relatively unknown author that recently received recognition for a bio on sculptor and suspected Crispin transference, Cindy Goddard. Wherever he is, or whoever he is, Crispin's pieces continue to serve as some of the most honest depictions of life and the human experience art has ever seen.

"The unpredictability of Crispin's work is what makes it so exciting," said Campton University fine art professor Marsha Grey in a 2015 lecture. "Like life, in all its randomness, its subtle and chaotic variations, through the depths of its misery and the pinnacle of its rapture, it is uncertain and anything but pedestrian. Even if it appears as tedious as Billy Fisher painting the George Washington Bridge for ten hours a day, every day. Or as page-seven as, Mary the baker overcoming self-hatred. Or Ashley Robins stashed underground, trying to make ends meet. And although often out of our control, these are the realities of our existence. We've all got a little Crispin in us, moving through the years, in and out of each other's lives. 'We're all works of art, with a reality to mind,' he once wrote. 'An unapologetic truth to bear. A sixty, seventy or so yearslong inner conversation between culture and identity.' And like with life and art, Crispin doesn't merely blur the line between existence and reality—he eliminates it."